Martha Evans Martin

The Ways of the Planets

Martha Evans Martin

The Ways of the Planets

1st Edition | ISBN: 978-3-75244-423-0

Place of Publication: Frankfurt am Main, Germany

Year of Publication: 2020

Outlook Verlag GmbH, Germany.

THE WAYS OF
THE PLANETS

BY

MARTHA EVANS MARTIN, A.M.

I

ON MAKING ACQUAINTANCE WITH THE PLANETS

It is sought in the following pages to give a simple account of what may now be said to be known of the character of the planets, and to describe with as little technicality as possible their movements and aspects and relations. An endeavor is made to impart concerning each one of them not, surely, profound learning, but just a good, every-day, practical notion, so that the mere name will call up a definite object, with its own attributes, appearance, and behavior, entirely distinct from any other planet or from any other object in the skies.

An endeavor is made also to so simplify and direct the observation that any one, after a little practice, will know almost without hesitation, on seeing a planet in the sky, that it is a planet, and not a fixed star, and exactly what planet it is. The situation and aspect of it will then as quickly and clearly pronounce it to be the individual planet that it is as the sight of a person of one's acquaintance proclaims him to be that person, and no other. The very name of Venus, for example, and still more the sight of Venus, will call up a conception of Venus, with the particular atmosphere and light and movements and wanderings which make her what she is. On looking at her the observer will at once know why she occupies the special position in the sky in which he sees her, why she is not so bright as she was when she was last in view, or is so much brighter than she was then, about how long she is likely to remain where she is, and when she goes what will become of her.

For far off and truly mysterious as the planets are, it still is with them as with most other objects in nature: a very little knowledge of their aspects and their ways begets a sense about them that makes the most casual observation of them interesting and, as far as it goes, intelligent. The slightest glance at them betrays some shape, or position, or light, or other quality, which at once makes recognition of them unmistakable. They disclose themselves oftentimes, one can scarcely say how, just as persons with whom we are intimate do by some half-caught outline, motion, or posture; or just as the trees do to an observer who knows, for example, an oak-tree from an elm, whether they are covered with their own peculiar verdure, or whether they stand with bare branches stretched out and colored in their own peculiar way.

2

This instant recognition of the planets is, of course, not to be had by simply reading about them. Such practical familiarity with them is attained only by seeking them out over and over again and looking at them with attention, with eagerness, and with all one's faculty. With them, as with other natural objects, it requires observation truly to know them. But then, observation, when one gets a little started in it, is a great deal more interesting, a great deal more absorbing, than any reading about them can ever be. It is also a very easy thing to begin, for, after all, it is not much more than looking and then looking again. In doing this one can hardly tell just when an object ceases to be strange, and then becomes familiar, and finally is so much a part of every-day knowledge that one knows it at a glance. But this is what happens in the case of any natural object when we observe it often and with true attention.

In the case of the planets, if one is interested at all, every stage in the cultivation of such an acquaintance is full of pleasure. Even to one who regards them only as a part of the general aspect of the sky, they are the most beautiful objects in it and always the first to attract special attention. Nine times out of ten, when any one asks what a certain star is, it proves to be one of the planets. When one of them is visible a person can hardly glance at the heavens without noticing it, even if he does not stop to think about it. But if he does stop to think about it and notices that it is far larger than any star he has noted before, that it hangs low in the western sky early in the evening, and shines with a brilliant silvery light, and if he then learns that it is Venus, will he not always have a pleasant thrill of recognition when he again sees such a star in such a position and knows it as Venus, among the planets as surpassing in beauty as the goddess of that name was among the immortals? Or, if in the east, at the same time in the evening, he sees a brilliant, solid-looking, unblinking star shining with a white light, but pinkish white, not silvery, and finds it to be Jupiter, will not such a star in such a situation be to him ever after a pleasant acquaintance that he can call by name? Not that Jupiter and Venus are always in these positions, or shine in just this way at all times. These are their places and aspects at certain times, frequently recurring, and at such times always unmistakably distinguish them.

It is, then, merely the matter of a little more and yet a little more observation, in order to come to know any one of the visible planets in all its varying aspects and situations. Of course, at the start some guidance is necessary, but only a little; and that little, if it is of the right sort, should not be irksome. To provide such guidance is one of the aims of this book. That is, indeed, its main aim.

But in addition to what, as a help in observation, it may find to say regarding the appearance and movements of the planets, it will endeavor to give also ample information concerning their character and constitution.

It is hoped that this may be done without weighting the narrative with figures, though some of the peculiarities of the planets must be expressed by means of numbers. Certainly no mathematical problems will be presented. But it will be profitable to remember that every one of the intimate things we know about the planets has come to us through the long and laborious mathematical work of astronomers. To them we owe the extinguishable debt that we owe to all special workers who put us in possession of the facts that interpret life to us.

For the astrology and poetry and romance of the planets one must go elsewhere. Nearly every book on the subject of the planets—and there are many of them—has some information about these things; and properly, too, for every genuine emotion and every real fancy has its value. But neither curious lore of the planets nor the sentiment and emotion they have produced in others is what the author of this book is striving to set forth. It is something much more vital than this. What we wish to contemplate here are the plain facts, the knowledge of which enlivens and enriches one's mind and nature. If the contemplation of them kindles one's fancy or excites one's emotions, these results at least will not be second-hand. If the bare facts, simply and plainly told, and the view of the planets themselves as they wander through their courses in the sky, do not awaken one's understanding and imagination, no amount of poetry or romance that other people have built up around the planets will arouse anything more than a factitious interest in them. It is when our own faculties are at work and our own fancy plays over a subject that we become genuinely and lastingly interested in it.

The facts themselves are in the main quite simple, and will not be given here as anything else than that. They have been fairly wrested from that mysterious thing called space by the mighty power of mind and unceasing labor. Our knowledge of them is due to long nights of watching and long days of calculating; to long and careful testing and considering of theories, only to find that something else must be tried; to courage to begin all over again, to sudden inspirations, and sometimes to those lucky discoveries that seem almost like miracles.

The subject of the planets has in some respects a greater interest even than that of the stars, because we know, after all, more about them. We sometimes have a feeling, though, that we know more of the stars, although the stars are so much farther off. Why we have this feeling it is easy to explain. Knowing them to be so far removed from us, we really approach the stars with a different expectation. The few things that we have learned about them have in themselves such a magnitude that it makes them seem a greater body of knowledge than they truly are. The stars are indeed so far away, and what we know of them has to be expressed in such large terms, that the mind does not demand in that information the minute exactness that it seeks for in the case of nearer objects.

In the case of the stars, we seek mainly to know their distances, the direction of their motions, the speed with which they travel, and their probable connection with each other. The fact that in computing the distance of a single star, many trillions of miles away, the result may be a little less than exact does not keep us from learning what ones are sufficiently near for their distances to be measured at all and what ones are immeasurably remote. Whether they travel at the rate of exactly three or three hundred miles a second, we can learn that some are traveling at somewhat the same rate of speed as our sun travels, and some incredibly faster; that certain groups are going in one direction and certain groups in another; that some are approaching us and some are receding from us. And thus we can classify them and learn the significance of these facts, and, little by little, gain a definite understanding of the construction and meaning of the entire universe. Their very remoteness gives a certain compactness to the information we have about the stars, by making it necessary to generalize more than we would if they were near enough to yield more details; and we are in a way satisfied with this more general sort of knowledge of them.

But the very fact of our knowing so much about the planets extends our curiosity concerning them and makes us feel that we ought to know more. The mind is provoked into more minute speculations about them, and we demand more exactness of information and knowledge of a more specific or intimate sort than would satisfy us in regard to the stars. Atmosphere, habitability, exact size, seasons, and day and night, are the kind of things we most seek to know in reference to the planets. These are such definite things that conclusions concerning them are subject to close criticism, and differences of opinion in regard to them thus sometimes occur which tend to give one a more or less confused notion of what is really known. As a matter of fact, our information about the planets is much fuller than our knowledge of the stars, as we would naturally expect it to be. Much of what we seek to know about the stars has long been common knowledge about the planets.

II

OUR RELATION TO THE PLANETS

To know about the planets is to know about ourselves. The earth is one of them. Whatever their origin, the earth's is the same. It and they are formed from the same nebula, controlled by the same central body, subject to the same laws, and destined for the same fate in the end. In this, the stars and the planets are not alike. They all shine upon us with the same sweet friendliness, and commonly we make no difference between them in our feeling for them. But the stars are bright and beautiful acquaintances living far away in their own domain. The planets are members of our own family, bone of our bone and flesh of our flesh, living comparatively near to us, within the domain of our common source of life, the sun.

One evening last autumn I was coming up Broadway, New York, with a friend, when we encountered at Union Square a man with a six-inch telescope directed toward the eastern sky. He was soliciting those who passed to stop and look at Mars and Saturn. Both of these planets were then very bright. They were also fairly near together, and so low in the east that one could scarcely help seeing them. But the people passed back and forth with hardly so much as a glance at the man and his telescope, and for the most part never even raised their eyes to the sky with a passing curiosity to see what it might be that he wanted to show them. My friend and I stopped and took each a view first of Mars and then of Saturn. While we were looking at the planets, a few of the passers-by began to loiter about, half smiling at us for so playing in public, slightly curious to see how we were faring at it, but for the most part apparently indifferent to what we were seeing. We had a fine view of Saturn lightly resting in his nest of rings, and an equally good view of the comical "eye" of Mars.

After we had finished, one or two others, evidently prompted by our example, followed us at the telescope. One or two inquired of us what the stars were that had so interested us, and one, pointing to Mars, wanted to know if it was Venus. As the crowd grew larger a few more ventured to take a look, much as they might venture to take their chance at hitting the bull's-eye in some shooting-gallery. With the telescope pointed at Saturn, the man droningly chanted: "This planet is 887,000,000 miles from the sun. The ring you see is

170,000 miles in diameter," and so on. These, to be sure, were the facts—and most marvelous facts, too—but without much meaning to one who knows nothing much about the planets; and the manner of their recital certainly did not make them alluring. I could not myself help feeling that the people there were missing a valuable opportunity, and that it would be only fair to them for some one fairly to cry out: "Come here and look at this planet. It is different from anything else you have ever seen or ever will see. It was at one time a part of the same nebulous mass that we were a part of. It is in the same system of worlds with us. It was formed in the same way that this world was formed. It is in itself the most wonderful thing you ever saw, and it is bound, as we are, to the sun by the ever-drawing tie of gravitation. The very position of our own world in space is more or less influenced by it. If anything should happen to it, it might be a serious matter to us."

For it is true that we are thus closely bound to the planets. The family tie among us is of far more force and significance than in any ordinary case of common origin. Human family ties wear, as we know, often into the merest threads, or even become no ties at all. But that between the earth and the planets remains apparently as close and strong as ever it was. The law of gravity, under which the earth draws toward its center every atom of matter surrounding it, and thus holds together all the atoms composing it, is not solely terrestrial in its application. It is probably universal. It certainly applies to every part of our little family of worlds. Every particle in the solar system attracts toward it every other particle in that system with a force determined by its mass and its distance. The sun, by reason of its immense size, compels the earth and all the other planets forever to circle around it. But the planets themselves have just as much power of attraction as the sun, atom for atom.

Thus, while the sun controls the motions of all of them, each pulls at the other, and, according to its power, determines how much the path of each shall vary from the course around the sun it otherwise would make. In the case of the smaller planets, this gravitational influence is, of course, very slight, and so subtle that we here on earth are not even conscious of it. But it is, nevertheless, real and continuous. It is greatest between the two largest planets, Jupiter and Saturn; but it was enough in the case of Uranus and Neptune to lead, by its mere manifestation on the earth, to the discovery of Neptune, the farthest planet.

Being thus of the same origin with the planets, having the same life history, being bound to them in space by a tie that is perhaps eternal, how can we fail to have the most intimate interest in their nature and all that concerns them?

But in addition to their close relationship to us there is, to make them of peculiar interest, the fact that, after the sun and the moon, they are for our eyes the most splendid objects in all the brilliant panorama of the sky. Such of them as we can see at all with the naked eye are most of the time much brighter than any first-magnitude star. As they wander from constellation to constellation the soft light of their placid faces gives a beauty and variety to the spectacle that endears them to us, and at the same time enhances by contrast their own charm and that of the glittering, unchanging stars.

There is nothing that gives one such a sense of sweet familiarity with the heavens as a really recognizing acquaintance with the planets. They are not, like the stars, associated with particular seasons. They come sometimes with the gay company of stars that dance their way across the cold winter skies, and sometimes with those that shine during the soft summer nights. Often in the spring and autumn we see some one of them before the sun is fairly down, and, before the light of an ordinary star can yet be seen, hanging in lone brilliancy as the evening star; and often an early riser has the reward of seeing one as a morning star glowing almost in the rays of the rising sun. Thus they are, one and another, with us at all times and seasons, and it accords with the fact of the relation being a family one that we have in their coming and going a sense of frequency and informality which we cannot have in the more regular and seasonal coming and going of the stars.

III

WHAT THE PLANETS ARE, AND WHAT THEY APPEAR TO BE

The planets are dark, opaque bodies which revolve at varying distances and at varying rates of speed in orbits more or less circular around the sun as a center. They have no light of their own, as the stars have, but shine wholly by reflected light received from the sun, which itself is a star. The amount of light they show to us depends upon their size, their distance, and their power of reflecting the light they receive.

In comparison with the stars, the planets are very near to us. Our sun, which is in constitution a star, but very widely separated from any other star in the universe, holds all his family of planets by the tether of gravitation, and so keeps them circling about him in a very small space, as astronomical space is measured. To all of the planets except Mercury, we ourselves are nearer than the sun is. To be sure, this distance between us and the planets, as measured by any terrestrial measure, is not exactly small. It is only by comparison that we can be said to have anything like a cozy relation to them. For merely earthly affairs we use terrestrial measures. In solar affairs we measure by an astronomical unit, which is the sun's distance from the earth, ninety-three millions of miles. When we say a planet's distance from the sun is thirty astronomical units, we mean it is thirty times farther than the earth is from the sun.

For matters outside of the solar system, the unit of measure is the number of miles that light travels in a year. The speed of light is a little more than 186,000 miles in a second. This is equal to about six trillions of miles in a year, or about sixty-three thousand times the distance of the sun from the earth, our family measuring-stick. From the nearest star it takes light more than four years to come to us. From the nearest planet light comes in less than three minutes, and from the farthest one it makes the journey in a little more than four hours.

As compared with other heavenly bodies, therefore, the sun and the planets are very near together, occupying a very small space in the immensity of the universe, immeasurably isolated from all the other systems and, so far as we know, immeasurably smaller as a system than most of them.

The whole body of the planets is divided according to size into two classes, the major and the minor planets. When we refer generally to the planets, the major planets only are meant. The minor planets are usually called the asteroids, or planetoids. There are many hundreds of them, and only one— and that barely—can be seen with the naked eye. The other planets are eight in number, including the earth, which is, after all, nothing but one of the smaller of the major planets. They are, in the order of their distances from the sun: Mercury, the nearest, Venus, the Earth, Mars, Jupiter, Saturn, Uranus, and Neptune. Of these only five—Mercury, Venus, Mars, Jupiter, and Saturn—can be seen from the earth without optical aid. Occasionally, when Uranus is very favorably situated, a person with an exceptionally good eye, who knows exactly where to look for the planet, can see it. Neptune is about equal to an eighth-magnitude star in brightness, and can never be seen without the aid of a telescope. Mercury, while quite bright enough to be seen, is not often situated favorably for observation. It is very near the sun, and is generally obscured either by the light of the sun when the sun and the planet are above the horizon, or by the haziness of the atmosphere when the sun is below the horizon and the planet a little above it. In regions of considerable altitude with a clear, rare atmosphere, Mercury is more often seen; but never for very long at a time.

The only planets, therefore, that are a part of our evening spectacle in the skies are Venus, Mars, Jupiter, and Saturn. These four happen to be not only the ones we oftenest see, but also the most interesting of all the planets from various points of view. Venus and Mars are the nearest to the earth, and most resemble it, and hence are the most inviting for speculations which have a human interest, such as habitability, the presence of life, and kindred ideas. Jupiter and Saturn are interesting above all the others in their splendor and size, and in their importance as the centers of systems of their own.

As seen by us, the planets are similar to the stars, but with very distinct differences in appearance, which, when once familiar, mark them so unmistakably as planets, and not fixed stars, that we need never get the two confused. The first and easiest distinguishing mark to notice is that they do not twinkle, as the stars do, but shine with a steady light similar to that of the moon. This is an invariable difference between stars and planets, and one needs only to stop and truly look at them in order to detect it. And once it has become familiar, it discloses itself at a glance.

This difference between stars and planets is due almost solely to difference of distance, though the twinkling is caused by our own atmosphere. The stars are too far away to send us anything but a mere point of light, and the unequal density of the waves of air sweeping over this point of light keeps it dancing before our eyes, causing the phenomenon that we call twinkling. But the planets, being nearer to us, show a disc, from every point of which comes a line of light, making the total light of some volume; and these inequalities of the air are too small to interfere with it to any extent. Sometimes, when the atmosphere is particularly unsteady, it happens that the light of a planet is somewhat affected by it when the planet is just rising or setting and is, consequently, near the horizon, and that it then seems to twinkle a little. But this departure from the rule is always slight and of short duration, in the case of the four planets most seen. Mercury, never being seen anywhere except near the horizon, often seems to twinkle; but then he is seldom seen at all, and, when visible, is in other ways so well marked that one cannot fail to recognize him.

So the steady light may justly be said to be invariable, because the unusual conditions are easily detected. When the atmosphere is such as to cause even the planets to blink a little, it has an effect also on the stars. At such a time they will appear to be fairly dancing. This effect is apt to occur on the clear nights of winter, the atmosphere being more unsteady then. Such nights, because of the extreme liveliness and brilliancy that they lend to the stars, are attractive times for amateur observations. For the astronomer, however, they are not so favorable. For the seeing of small details such as he seeks, the steadiest atmosphere is necessary.

Though the planets are near enough to show a disc, they are not sufficiently near to show to the naked eye as sharp an outline as the moon's. Usually the edge is more or less rayed like that of a fixed star, which adds somewhat to the difficulty of distinguishing them from the stars until their aspect has become familiar to us. The fact that we are looking at a disc is plainly shown when an occultation by the moon occurs. When the moon occults a fixed star, it passes between us and the star. At such times the star disappears behind the edge of the moon instantly, as a mere point naturally would. When a planet is occulted by the moon, it disappears gradually as the moon covers more and more of its disc, thus showing unmistakably the nature of it.

After steadiness of shining, the next most obvious mark of difference between a planet and a star, from our point of view, is the movement of the planets. A star remains always in one place with relation to the other stars, while the planets move about from constellation to constellation, seeming to travel sometimes toward the east and sometimes toward the west.

This difference also is due solely to a difference of distance. The stars as well as the planets are constantly in motion. Most of them, in truth, move at a rate which would make the rate of motion of a planet a mere snail's pace in comparison. Arcturus, for instance, is supposed to be moving at the rate of two or three hundred miles a second, and there are other fixed stars with an equally rapid motion. The swiftest moving of the planets does not achieve much more than twenty-nine miles a second, while the slowest swings along at a rate of but little more than three miles in the same length of time.

These are the real rates of speed of the stars and planets; but they are not at all what they seem to us. The difference in distance is so great that for centuries and centuries the flying stars have seemed to men to remain in the same place in the skies, and so we call them fixed. The planets, so slow-journeying as they are in comparison, seem to us to be moving among the constellations at rates varying from more than a degree a day in the swiftest to between two and three degrees a year in the slowest.

Hence, if through lack of practice in observation a person is not at once able to distinguish the difference between the stars and the planets in the character of their light—that is, whether they twinkle or shine steadily—he can, by taking a little longer time, at most only a few days, determine whether the object he sees is a star or a planet by noticing whether it has any motion among the other stars. Venus and Mars will show some movement in one evening. Jupiter and Saturn may require a little more time to disclose their motion.

IV

THE ORIGIN OF THE PLANETS

Different as the planets are as individuals, they have too many characteristics in common to admit any question of their common origin. They are not simply stars of one sort and another that happen to lie nearer to us than the great body of stars that spangle the heavens, but are, without doubt, all of one family with us in their origin, as well as in their situation. How they originated, and exactly what has been their course of evolution, has long been an engrossing problem among philosophers; and it is not yet solved.

In the sense that the human race is all of one family, the planets are but a part of the great universe that lies about us and is in part visible to us. The forms in which we know matter as existing in the universe, outside of the solar system and of the minor forms in our own world, are those of stars and nebulæ. It seems as if either of these could, and in fact does, form out of the other. We do not at all know how in the beginning matter took the form of either, or which came first. But it is believed that a star is formed by the condensation of a nebula, and that a nebula is often formed by the collision or near approach of two stars and the consequent disintegration of their particles.

The sun is a star not very different from most of the other stars, as we believe them to be, except that it is smaller than most of them. It is the center around which we and all the planets revolve, and it is believed that we were all once a part of the very body of it. For astronomers are substantially agreed that the whole solar family, including the sun and all the planets, has been evolved from a great nebula which, in one form or another, at one time filled practically the whole of the immense space from the sun to the outermost planet of the system. While this cannot be said to have been exactly proved, yet it accords with all the known facts of the solar system. As to how this nebula originated, and what its shape was, and in just what way the planets were formed from it, there is more diversity of opinion.

Up to the middle of the eighteenth century no really scientific theory of the evolution of the solar system was formulated, and it was not until the very last years of that century that any theory of the origin of the planets was published which received anything like universal acceptance.

This was the case, however, with the famous nebular hypothesis of Laplace, which was published in 1796, and for a time seemed so nearly to account for the various phenomena of the motions and relations of the planets that it was not only accepted in the scientific world, but became almost as much a part of universal knowledge as that the earth is round. But even this theory has not completely stood the test of time, which inevitably brings that close scientific investigation that any theory must undergo when it is used as a working basis to which all facts and secondary theories must be correlated.

The original nebular hypothesis supposed this vast nebula to be in rotation on its axis. As it condensed, the falling-in of the particles caused its rotation to become more rapid, until finally, under the strain of this, a ring of matter was "thrown off" from the outer edge. Or, as was sometimes said, the inner part condensed and left a detached ring of matter. This ring, continuing to rotate in the direction given it by the rotation of the central mass, finally condensed into a planet, rotating on its axis and revolving about the central sun in the same direction as the ring had revolved. The satellites of the planets were thought to have been formed by the same process from the planets while these were still in a plastic state. Saturn, with its wonderful system of rings and satellites, was thought to be a minute object-lesson of a planet in course of evolution, and this we have often heard said.

I am sorry it is not so. I had much enthusiasm in my youth over this beautiful and orderly arrangement of things: first, the splendid hypothesis, the achievement of a noble mind; then the little model showing the work in its progress; and, finally, the beautifully finished system, the rings all rolled up into planets, traveling unceasingly in paths which eternally marked the size of the central body, or sun, at the time of the separation.

But it is now pretty certain that this cannot be the way it all happened. Closer investigation shows that there are mechanical difficulties which were not at first fully recognized. A series of rings could not have been left off by a body so wholly gaseous. The particles composing them would not be sufficiently coherent to permit of separation in any such compact, uniform, and decisive manner. Then, even if such a ring were thrown off, it is not at all certain that it could condense into a planet. Its tendency, indeed, would be to disintegrate rather than to condense. In a body so tenuous the mutual gravitation of its particles would be too feeble to complete the work. Besides, in conflict with the theory is the fact that a few of the satellites of the planets revolve in a direction contrary to that of the planet. And there are other minor, but still important, details in the mechanism of the solar system which cannot be accounted for by the ring theory.

And so, while astronomers are still agreed that the whole solar system, which includes the planets, was evolved from a primeval nebula, the theory of leaving off rings which condensed into planets is not found tenable, and the search for some more acceptable theory or some modification of the Laplace theory is now occupying a number of eminent astronomers and philosophers.

The result of all this is that no theory of the manner of the evolution of the planets is definitely accepted by the body of astronomers. Much hard labor and ingenious reasoning have been expended in endeavoring to formulate some hypothesis by means of which we may account for observed phenomena. The astronomers with whom these theories have originated are, naturally, more or less ardent in setting them forth. Thus one occasionally sees a decisive and authoritative statement of a theory of the evolution of the planets that seems at first view to account for everything. But no one of these has yet been entirely accepted by astronomers, who are as a class cautious and conservative, and are necessarily critical of any theory, because the value of much of their future work depends upon its accuracy and sufficiency for all details.

The theory which at present seems more nearly than any other to offer a reasonable explanation of most planetary phenomena is based upon the supposition that the nebula from which the sun and planets were evolved was in the shape of a spiral, and not the gaseous mass that the original nebular hypothesis supposed. The fact that among the many thousands of nebulæ that have been discovered and observed a very large proportion of them are in this form, aside from any other consideration, suggests a great probability that the one from which the solar system was evolved was a spiral.

The spiral nebulæ seem to be of a somewhat different constitution from the other nebulæ, and show on observation spots of condensation here and there, which at least suggest the formation of systems of planets. This indicates that ours may be only one of many such systems in process of evolution; but it is certainly among the smallest of them, for most of the spiral nebulæ are immensely greater in size than the one required to form our little system. Its few trillions of miles of diameter, though it seems so vast to us, is quite insignificant in comparison with a large proportion of the spiral nebulæ in the universe.

15

A spiral nebula is in the form of a disc somewhat resembling that familiar form of fireworks known as a pinwheel. The typical form of it has two arms projecting from opposite sides of the whirling figure. It is much denser toward the center, where the spiral would naturally be more tightly wound, and has smaller spots of condensation scattered like knots here and there along the fiery arms. In the process of evolution the denser center becomes the controlling sun, and the smaller spots of condensation form the planets, which are eventually detached from the revolving mass, but continue to revolve about the center as they were doing from the beginning. According to the mass it has in the beginning, the planet gathers up by gravitative attraction all the material in its region, gaseous or more or less condensed, and grows by this accretion. If the nucleus happened to be a large one before it separated from the parent body, it will have sufficient force of gravitation to gather in large quantities of material and greatly increase its size, and thus become a large planet. If it is only a small nucleus, it has less power of attraction, and gathers in less material.

When these condensations of matter which are the nuclei of the planets break away from the parent body, they sometimes carry with them still smaller nuclei, which, if they are not too near the original center, or sun, are destined to remain under the control of the planets and become their satellites. The number and size of the satellites a planet has depends upon the size, and hence the controlling force, of the nucleus which is its foundation, and also upon the number of spots of condensation that chanced to be formed in its neighborhood sufficiently near to come under the gravitational control of the planet. If by any chance the nucleus which was to form the largest satellite of Jupiter had been in the situation of Mercury, for instance, it might well have given its allegiance to the sun, instead of to Jupiter, and thus have become a planet.

Under the ring theory the outermost planet, Neptune, would be the oldest of the planet family, and the one nearest the sun, Mercury, would be the latest born and youngest. But the physical development of these planets seems to indicate, in truth, exactly the opposite of this, as we shall see later on. Under the spiral-nebula theory the planets may be nearly of the same age, their different states of development being due mainly to difference in size and to some peculiarities of situation. If the nucleus happened to be near the outer edge of the spiral, it would be formed from the lighter matter composing the outer part of the nebula, and this seems to be the case with the outer planets. If it were near the dense center of the nebula, it would be composed of denser material, and this seems to be so in the case of the inner planets.

A nebula, it is thought, is formed by the collision or the near approach of two of the many stars, or suns, that we know are traveling about at high velocities as vagrants here and there through space. If the two bodies come together centrally, the force of the impact will generate heat sufficient to convert them into a nebula; but this will not necessarily be spiral in form. If they come together obliquely, the chances are that they will form into a rapidly rotating spiral disc.

But in order to form a spiral, it is not necessary that there should be an actual collision. Because of the force of gravitation the near approach of two stars would subject them to an enormous strain from their pull upon each other, and there is a limit within which they cannot approach without being literally torn to pieces from the effect of this tidal force. Even if they do not approach within this fatal limit, which is a little less than two and one-half times the radius of the body, they may come so near as to change their character entirely, and, through their tidal influence on each other, form into a rotating spiral nebula with two arms projecting from opposite sides of the spiral.

It now seems probable that it was after this manner that the sun and its family of planets were formed. The matter which is contained in them may have been in the form of a dark, solid body pursuing some sort of course in space. In its journeying it came near another body and was awakened into a life of activity in the form of a flat, spiral nebula which was left spinning around in a pyrotechnic manner, the matter composing it much diffused at the outer edges and densest in the center. Scattered through it were the more or less condensed spots which were the embryonic forms destined to come forth from the parent body as the individual planets.

When the separation was completed, each planet fed and grew upon all the matter that it had the force to draw to it, and it swept clean the space that lay within the limits of its power. If the particles thus gathered in were small and slow of motion, they became a part of the body of the planet. If they were large and swift, they became members of the planet's family as satellites. In whatever area of the nebula each planet came into a separate existence, it fed upon the matter which that area afforded. In the case of Neptune, at the outer edge of the system, it was very diffuse matter; in Mercury's region, nearer the center, it was more dense.

Thus in our family of planets, though its members were born of the same parent and developed under the same guiding laws, each has a distinct individuality arising from its inherent qualities and its environment during the early stages of its existence. The spiral-nebula theory seems to offer a better explanation of these individual qualities than any other that has been advanced thus far, and in its main features it is pretty generally accepted. But one must keep in mind that the details of any theory of the beginning and growth of the planets are more or less speculative, or, at least, have not yet been proved with finality.

V

THE SEVEN GREAT PLANETS

So far as we know, five of the planets—Mercury, Venus, Mars, Jupiter, and Saturn—have been known from time immemorial. There are existing records of them made thousands of years ago. There is no reason why they should not have been thus known, since they have always been as they are now, visible to the naked eye, and all of them save Mercury are as easily seen as the sun or the moon. They do not, of course, exact the instant attention that those great luminaries do, because, being smaller, they are less isolated from the great body of the stars; but they are in their seasons plainly visible, and can then always be seen if one looks at them.

In ancient times, when people lived more out-of-doors than is the habit now, they did look at them. The same primitive shepherds that, while tending their flocks at night on the hills, named the constellations according to the fanciful shapes that the unchanging stars seemed to outline, watched also the five wandering stars, more wonderful to them than any of the others. They observed how mysteriously these stars came at certain seasons and silently threaded their way across the shining heavens, and then as mysteriously disappeared. They saw them not only differing from the other stars in glory, but changing in their own brilliancy from one time to another, until, in some cases, they failed to recognize them as the same stars under varying aspects. Venus, for instance, they called Phosphorus, or Lucifer, when they saw her as a morning star, and Hesperus, or Vesper, when she shone in the evening.

The sun and the moon, they noted, also moved from place to place among the fixed stars, and they called all these errant bodies planets, which means "wanderers." These are the "seven planets" referred to in the earlier literatures and in all early books on astronomy or astrology. This is sometimes a little confusing, because, though the sun and the moon are no longer called planets, we still (omitting the earth) have seven. But Neptune and Uranus, not being visible to the naked eye, were not known to the ancients. They were discovered by means of the telescope, and that only within the last century and a half. So, owing to these comparatively new-found members of the solar family, we have yet the magic number of planets, seven.

These seven are the major planets and the ones with which mainly it will be our endeavor here to promote and strengthen an acquaintance. With Uranus and Neptune the acquaintance will necessarily be less intimate than with the others, because we cannot see them in the same free way; but they are not on this account much less interesting than the others, and a little knowledge of them is pleasant family history. They simply do not live within sight.

The planets that are nearer to the sun than we are, and hence lie between us and the sun, are called the inferior, or sometimes interior, planets. Those that lie outside the orbit of the earth are called the superior, or the exterior, planets. In so grouping them the earth is the dividing-point, and is not itself in either class. Mercury and Venus are the inferior planets. The superior planets are Mars, Jupiter, Saturn, Uranus, and Neptune. The distinction has importance, especially when we are discussing the planets with relation to their movements, as seen from the earth, because the planets with orbits between us and the sun (the inferior planets) have very different phases and apparent motions from those whose orbits are beyond us from the sun (the superior planets).

When considered in regard to size, constitution, development, and their likeness to each other, the planets are sometimes distinguished as the terrestrial planets and the major planets. This need occasion no confusion with the general division of them into major and minor planets, because, as has been said, when simply "the planets" are mentioned, these seven large planets are always the ones that are meant, the others being usually called asteroids, or planetoids. The terrestrial planets are Mercury, Venus, Earth, and Mars. As the name implies, they are so called because they are in some respects similar to the earth. The major planets are Jupiter, Saturn, Uranus, and Neptune. They are all larger than the terrestrial planets, and, in addition, have some other characteristics in common which the planets of the other group do not have. The two classes represent different stages of evolution.

The four planets forming the terrestrial group are sometimes called the inner planets, and the four major planets are then known as the outer planets. The point of division in mind then is the space between Mars and Jupiter. This is so vast in comparison with the spaces between the other planets from the sun out to Mars that it becomes a convenient dividing-line, particularly as the groups divided by it are in some respects essentially different from each other.

Of the four planets which have an especial interest to us because of their being the ones most easily seen, two are terrestrial, or inner, planets, Mars and Venus, and two are major, or outer, planets, Jupiter and Saturn. The differences between the two classes are solely matters of constitution and situation, and have nothing to do with their appearance to us. Venus, the brightest of them all, belongs to one group; Jupiter, the second in brilliancy, belongs to the other.

That there is at least one other planet beyond the present boundary of our system (which is the orbit of Neptune) seems to be quite probable. Some astronomers think there may be several others. There are certain perturbations, or irregularities, in the movements of Neptune which the influence of Uranus does not account for, and they seem to indicate that there is some disturbing body even beyond the orbit of that farthest known planet.

Several astronomers are working on the problem of locating this undiscovered body. At various times it has been announced that such a planet would probably be found in a certain position in the skies at a specified date; but as yet no one has been able to get a view of it. Recently the orbit of a far-off hypothetical planet has been calculated, and its place predicted for 1914. Perhaps it may be found then. Of course it could never be seen through any but the most powerful telescopes. Its calculated distance from the sun is one hundred and five times that of the earth. This would be more than nine billions of miles, or more than three times farther than Neptune is from the sun. It would require fourteen hours for light to pass from the sun to a planet at that distance, and the sun would appear to it smaller than Saturn or an ordinary first-magnitude star does to us.

A further reason for suspecting the existence of such a planet is suggested by the orbits of certain comets. These erratic bodies, when they chance to come within the bounds of the solar system, are sometimes forced to remain because of the powerful influence of one of the planets near which their path has taken them. Jupiter holds as many as thirty of them in this way, Saturn and Uranus have two or three, and Neptune has captured as many as six. But there are still others that return to us in regular periods, but which go sufficiently far beyond Neptune to escape entirely if there were not some still more distant watch-dog to turn them back. So there seems good reason to believe that Neptune is not really the outermost of the planets.

There has also been much said about the possibility of a planet nearer to the sun than Mercury. When Mercury is at perihelion, or nearest to the sun, there are certain irregularities in his movements which might be explained by the presence of another planet between Mercury and the sun. In 1859 it was thought that such a planet had been observed. Its time of revolution and its distance from the sun were estimated, and it was named Vulcan. In some of the books of astronomy published about that time, and even in some published as many as fifteen years later, Vulcan is mentioned as a reality. But now it is believed that the observation was a mistake, and no such body is known to exist.

In 1878 it was again thought that two bodies nearer to the sun than Mercury had been discovered during an eclipse. These observations have never been explained or confirmed; but it is thought that the objects seen were probably stars which were mistaken for planets by the observers. If a body so situated does exist, it is so near the sun that it probably can never be seen except during an eclipse, and the time of observation is then so short and mistakes are so easily made that it is difficult to verify the observation. The continued search for the cause of the perturbations of Mercury may finally lead to the discovery of something between it and the sun. But if it is a single body, this seems a much less promising task than the search for a planet, or planets, on the outer edge of the solar system.

VI

THE MOVEMENTS OF THE PLANETS

In considering the movements of the planets, we have to regard their actual motion in space and that motion as it appears to us. They all have two principal motions in space. They revolve about the sun in their orbits, and they rotate on their axes. The manner in which they accomplish the rotation on their axes determines the length of their days and nights, or whether, indeed, they shall have any such grateful alternations of light and darkness. Those planets which, like the earth, turn on their axes in less time than they make their journey around the sun have one day and one night every time they make a complete rotation. Those that turn on their axes in the same time that they revolve around the sun, of which sort there seems to be at least one, face always toward the sun, and have no alternations of day and night. On one side it is always day; on the other it is always night. The number of days a planet has during each revolution around the sun depends upon how much time it requires to make a revolution, and how fast it spins on its axis. In one year here on the earth we have three hundred and sixty-five days and nights. Saturn, in its year, has more than twenty-three thousand days and nights.

The manner in which the revolution of the planets in their orbits takes place determines the length and character of their year; the nearer a planet is to the sun, the shorter its orbit is, and the faster the rate of speed at which the sun compels it to move, and hence the shorter its year. The nearest of the planets, Mercury, makes more than five hundred revolutions around the sun, while the farthest, Neptune, makes one. Three times in a year—that is, a terrestrial year —the nearest planet speeds around its orbit and back to the starting-place with seventeen days to spare. One hundred and sixty-five terrestrial years are necessary for the farthest planet to make one circuit of its orbit. The first goes at the average rate of nearly thirty miles a second over a path more than two hundred million miles long. The second travels a path more than seventeen billion miles in length, at the average rate of three and four-tenths miles a second. Between these two extremes the other planets have orbits and rates of speed varying with their distances from the sun. The farther they are from the sun, the larger the orbit and the slower the speed.

To get something like a picture of the sun and the planets as they actually lie and as they move in space, one should have in mind an immense flat, circular disc five and a half billions of miles in diameter passing through the sun, which is in the center of it. Around the edge of the disc is the orbit through which Neptune moves. At varying distances inside of it are the orbits of the other planets, each growing smaller and smaller as one comes nearer and nearer to the sun, until the orbit of Mercury, the planet nearest to the sun, is reached.

Since it is not a hard metal disc that we are considering, but only an imaginary one in space, there may be a little latitude allowed for the orbits to tip somewhat out of the exact plane of the disc without materially altering the figure in mind. And this they do, very slightly—most of them to the extent only of from one to two degrees, though one of them falls outside of the common plane about seven degrees. In these orbits all the planets, as seen from the sun, are going around from west to east. At the same time they are turning on their axes in the same direction, some standing almost erect, as it were, in their orbits and whirling like a dancing dervish as they skim along, and others more or less inclined like a traveling top.

The time a planet requires to make one circuit of its orbit constitutes, as with the earth, its year. But we who are on the earth have, in our study of another planet, to regard it as having in a sense two years. First, there is the time it takes, starting from a given point in its orbit, to circle around the sun and return to that point. This is known as its sidereal period, or year, and is so called from *sidus*, meaning a star, because the only way to mark any point in space is by a fixed star, and, as viewed from the sun, one revolution of a planet would be from a given star back again to that star.

Then there is the time a planet takes, starting when it is in a straight line with the earth and the sun in space, to return to the place where the three bodies will be again in the same relative position. This is known as its synodic period, or year. Synodic is from our word synod, meaning a meeting or assembly, and the synodic year is the time between two successive and similar meetings of these three bodies. The sidereal year concerns the planet in its relation to the sun; the synodic year, in its relation to the earth. The synodic year is the only one that much concerns us while regarding the planets as a part of the spectacle of the sky. It is the one that we know from observation, while the sidereal year is mathematically computed.

The two periods, or years, are not of the same length, because the sun with reference to the planet is always stationary, and the motion resulting in the sidereal year is that of the planet only, while the synodic year is the result of the movements of both the earth and the planet, each, in its own orbit, being always in motion.

An inferior planet, situated as it is nearer to the sun than the earth is, and so having a shorter orbit than the earth's, will, when it finishes its sidereal year and comes around to the point from which it started, find the earth advanced from that position and will, therefore, have to travel farther on in order to overtake it and come into the same relative position from which they started, which makes the time of its circuit with reference to the earth obviously longer than with reference to the sun.

With the superior planets the case is just reversed. The earth is the inside planet, or the one nearest the sun, and it must overtake *them*. With one exception, they are all so far away from the sun and move so slowly that it takes us but little more than one of our years to overtake them and bring them into the same relative position with us that they had when we started, while it requires many of our years for any one of them to make a single circuit of the sun. Hence their circuit with reference to the earth is shorter than with reference to the sun.

With Mars, the exception referred to, we have a more hardly fought race. That planet is not so far from us as are the other superior planets. It makes its revolution around the sun in a little less than two of our years. We travel eighteen miles a second, and it travels fifteen miles in the same length of time. If we are in line with it at the beginning of our journey, we glide off swiftly, and easily leave it far behind. When, however, we come back to the starting-point, it has not loitered, and is many millions of miles ahead of us, and it remains ahead until more than seven weeks after we have returned to the starting-point a second time. Fifty days after we have begun to make our third round we overtake it, and are again in a direct line with the planet and the sun. This makes its period with reference to the earth ninety-three days longer than its own year, and fifty days longer than two of ours. This is the longest synodic period among the planets.

The orbits in which the planets move all have the form of an ellipse—that is, of a circle more or less flattened. This flattening, or the extent to which an orbit departs from the form of a true circle, is called its eccentricity. The sun is never at the exact center of an orbit, but is always situated a little to one side of the center—that is, it is at one of the foci of the ellipse. Consequently, the planet, as it travels in its orbit, is not always at the same distance from the sun, the amount of the variation in distance depending upon the eccentricity of the orbit. The point in the orbit where the planet is nearest to the sun is its perihelion, and the point at which it is farthest is its aphelion. It is necessary to keep these elementary facts in mind in order fully to understand the changes in the motions and brightness of the planets.

The influence of one body over another that is circling around it is to make it move faster or more slowly according to its distance from the central body. Since a planet varies in its distance from the sun in the different parts of its orbit, it is forced to move fastest when it is in that part of the orbit which is nearest to the sun, and slowest when it is in the part farthest away. In other words, the motion of a planet is more rapid at perihelion than at aphelion. The earth is in perihelion, or nearest to the sun, in winter—that is, winter in the northern latitudes—and in consequence it moves faster in winter than in summer, and the northern winters are, for this reason, a little shorter than the summers.

These two simple movements of the planets—that around the sun and that on their axes—are their principal real movements, and are such as they would show to be if seen from the sun, which is the center of them. There are also certain minor real movements arising from various causes, one being the influence that the planets exercise on one another; but for the ordinary observer these have no particular significance. Then, the planets all share the one grand movement which the sun itself is known to be making through limitless space to a destination of which we are in utter ignorance, over even a path which we know nothing of save that it leads toward the bright star Vega, in the constellation of the Lyre. As the sun moves on in that direction at the rate of eleven miles a second he takes with him all his family of planets and planetoids, with their satellites, and whatever other bodies have their abode in his domain. Thus they travel as a body, each individual spinning on its axis, from the sun itself down to the smallest planetoid, the satellites circling around the planets, and the planets in their turn around the sun. And in all these movements the earth takes part as one of the planets. The sun itself is following a comparatively straight line in space, and, so far as we know, in allegiance to no other body. It is, though, just possible that this comparatively straight line may be the arc of a circle so vast that we have not yet had time to discover its curvature, and that the sun itself may be pursuing its own circuit around some still more powerful body.

VII

HOW THE INFERIOR PLANETS SEEM TO MOVE

Of the real movements of the planets, as described in the last chapter, we get here on the earth only a very fragmentary view. Without the aid of the telescope none of them is visible to us except the movements in their orbits, and these, to our view, are somewhat different from the simple, circling course apparent to an observer on the sun. The difference is due to the fact that the earth itself is always in movement in just the same way that the other planets are, and we, being never at any time at the center of the orbits, do not see the movements of the planets as they truly take place, but only as they are outlined against the sky. So the appearances and disappearances and visible travels among the stars by which we know the planets are only as we see them. Some knowledge of the real movements is necessary to a proper understanding of the apparent movements; but it is only with the latter that, for ordinary observation, we need to be particularly acquainted.

The rotation of the earth on its axis, as we know, causes the familiar daily apparent rising, passing, and setting of all the heavenly bodies. In this apparent motion the planets share as well as the sun, moon, and stars. But it is their movement *among* the fixed stars, and not *with* them, that distinguishes them as planets, and this it is necessary to know in order to keep track of them and be able to recognize them in their varying places and guises. For they sometimes shine in their greatest glory in one season, and sometimes in another, and at the recurrence of the same season they are sometimes in one part of the sky and sometimes in another, so that their ways of coming and going border almost on the mysterious, until one learns the manner of this apparent vagrancy. Happily, this knowledge is easily attained, and then the matter is simple enough.

The apparent motions of the inferior planets, Mercury and Venus, always take place near the sun. Venus never wanders more than forty-eight degrees from it, and Mercury never more than twenty-eight. Most of the time they are much nearer than this. Since we cannot see either of them except when the sun is below the horizon, the consequence of their being always thus near to him is that they are in view for only a short time after the sun has set or before he has risen. If they are in the evening sky, and hence east of the sun, they soon follow him when he sinks below the western horizon. If they are west of the sun, and, consequently, are the first to rise in the morning, it is not long before his brilliant rays flood with light the eastern sky and blot the planets from our view. Venus can be seen sometimes for three hours at a time, Mercury for never more than one. Within this limited region of the sky they appear to journey evening by evening away from the sun, somewhat obliquely, but toward the zenith, until they have reached the end of their tether. Then they journey back and pass to the other side of the sun. There they climb their path toward the zenith, moving westward and, as we see them, obliquely upward. Morning by morning they get farther from the sun until their westward limit of freedom is reached, when they again draw in toward the sun, pass it, appear in the evening sky, and pull off up the sky toward the east again. Thus they swing from east to west of the sun, and back again, in unceasing repetition.

As they pass the sun going from east to west—that is, from the evening to the morning sky—the inferior planets go between us and the sun; and when they swing back from west to east, or from the morning to the evening sky, they pass on the side of the sun farthest away from us. When they are in a direct line with the earth and the sun they are said to be in conjunction. If at this point they are between us and the sun, it is inferior conjunction. If they are on the other side of the sun, they are said to be in superior conjunction. When the planet, as seen in the evening, has traveled toward the east as far from the sun as it will go during that particular revolution, it is said to be at its greatest eastern elongation. Elongation means simply apparent distance from the sun; hence, greatest eastern elongation is the greatest distance possible east of the sun from our point of view. Greatest western elongation, which we see in the morning before dawn, occurs when the planet is at its greatest apparent distance west of the sun.

While apparently drawing near and then away from the sun, traveling obliquely up and down the evening and the morning sky, the planet has all the time been moving in one direction around the sun; but we could see the motion only as it appeared on the background of the sky. The planet is in reality just as far from the sun when it is in conjunction as at elongation. The difference is that we see it at a different angle, or from a different point of view. But it has not been at all times equally near to the earth.

When an inferior planet is at greatest eastern elongation, it is, of course, east of the sun, and can be seen above the sun in the evening after sunset, and is an evening star. As it moves westward nearer and nearer to the sun, it is above the horizon a proportionately shorter time each evening, and is more and more obscured by the sun's rays until it reaches inferior conjunction, when it is exactly between us and the sun, and hence at the point nearest to us. Here it becomes invisible, largely because it has its dark side toward us, but partly because the dazzling light of the sun entirely obscures it. Once in a while our relative positions are such that we see it pass like a black dot directly over the bright face of the sun. This is called a transit. But a transit does not occur at every inferior conjunction. It would so occur if the planet's orbit and the earth's were in exactly the same plane. But the small tilt that they have is sufficient to throw the planet, when it is passing the sun, into such an angle that it does not pass directly between the disc of the sun and us, but a little above or below. Thus transits are rather rare, though they occur periodically in the case of both Venus and Mercury, and will be spoken of elsewhere.

When the planet has passed inferior conjunction, it is then west of the sun, and rises in the morning before the sun is up, and is a morning star. For a few days it can be seen either not at all or with difficulty. Then, as it works its way out of the rays of the sun and on toward the west, it rises earlier each morning until it reaches its farthest point west.

As it starts back east again its distance from the earth increases daily until it reaches its greatest distance from us at superior conjunction. It is then the whole diameter of its orbit farther from us than when it was at inferior conjunction, and it is again invisible. The illuminated side of it is toward us; but it is at its smallest, because it is at its greatest distance from us, and even when it is not directly behind the sun the light of that luminary is too great for successful competition. After it has passed superior conjunction it is again in the evening sky, apparently moving farther from the sun each day. It is at the same time actually coming nearer to us each day, and these two facts cause a daily increase in its brightness.

But an inferior planet is not, like the superior planets and the stars, brightest when it is nearest to us. It is, in fact, darkest when it is nearest—that is, when it is at inferior conjunction—and we cannot see it at all. This is because an inferior planet passes through phases, like the moon, changing gradually during its rounds from full to crescent, and back again. Its full face is toward us when it is on the opposite side of the sun and farthest from us. The proportion of the face that is illuminated grows smaller as the planet approaches its eastern elongation. But the planet grows brighter because it is coming nearer to us and is getting out of the dazzling rays of the sun. One-half of its surface is illuminated when it is at greatest elongation; but it is brightest a few days later, when less than half of its face is illuminated, because it is enough nearer to compensate for the slight diminution in the proportion of light on its disc. It is brightest in the morning a short time before its western elongation, for the same reason.

This in a general way describes the motion of an inferior planet, and this is all that we need to know in order to understand its ordinary visible movements. If we watch it carefully, however, we may detect that shortly before inferior conjunction it pauses in its onward sweep and seems for a time to be stationary, and then to retrace its way among the stars until a short time after inferior conjunction, when it again pauses and appears stationary, and finally starts off again in its original direction on its way toward greatest western elongation. During this capricious sort of progress the planet usually describes more or less of a loop, sometimes almost a flourish, in its path. The appearance is wholly due to the planet's overtaking and passing us in our journey around the sun. For a time it travels behind us, then beside us, and then beyond us; and, since we are both in motion, the effect is much the same as when one train passes another while they are both traveling in the same direction. The orbits of the earth and the planet are not exactly in the same plane, and, both bodies being in motion, we are not in a position to see the planet at the same angle more than once as it seems to pass back and forth, and so we get the effect of its making a flourish or loop. But this effect, while interesting, takes place only when the planet is so near the sun that to the ordinary observer it itself does not count for much. We can see but little of the inferior planets at that time, anyway, though it is important for us to know where they are, in order to keep track of them and to be ready for them when they are to be seen.

VIII

HOW THE SUPERIOR PLANETS SEEM TO MOVE

The movements of the superior planets, Mars, Jupiter, Saturn, Uranus, and Neptune, as they appear to us, are different from those of the inferior planets in some important respects. Instead of swinging back and forth east and west of the sun, and never appearing very far away from it, as the inferior planets do, the superior planets make an entire circuit of the heavens, and it is possible to see them at any distance from the sun, and at any time during the night. Sometimes they are, with relation to the earth, in that part of the sky exactly opposite to the sun, and hence in line with it and the earth. At such times they can be seen all night. They are then said to be in opposition, and are in the best position for our observation. The earth being, when in this situation, in a direct line between them and the sun, we have the sun at our backs, as it were, shedding its full rays on the disc of the planet under observation, which is then at its nearest to us, and also at its brightest. For, since the orbits of all the superior planets are outside of ours, the planets never get between us and the sun, and, in consequence, never turn a dark side toward us. Their entire discs are practically always illuminated, and their changes in brightness depend largely upon their changes in distance, which, as we have seen, is not the case with the inferior planets.

Mars, the nearest of them, is at times somewhat gibbous (that is, shows a little less than a full face, as the moon does when just beginning to wane), and, in less degree, Jupiter also. But in neither case is this departure from fullness sufficient to have any appreciable effect on the planet's brightness, and, moreover, it does not occur when the planet is in the most favorable position for us to see it. At opposition, therefore, we always have the full face of the planet presented to us; and being, as we then are, on the same side of the sun with it, we are ninety-three millions of miles (our distance from the sun) nearer to it than the sun is.

Being, when in opposition, exactly opposite the sun, the planet rises just as the sun sets. After opposition it rises a little earlier each evening, and is higher up in the sky at each succeeding sunset. When we find it just half-way between the eastern and the western horizon at sunset, it is at quadrature. After quadrature it appears nearer and nearer the western horizon each evening at sunset, until it finally is too near the sun to be visible. It is then traveling in that part of its orbit which is beyond the sun from us. From opposition to this situation it has been an evening star.

When a superior planet is in line with the sun and the earth, and is on the far side of the sun from us, it is said to be in conjunction, and we are then one hundred and eighty-six millions of miles, or twice our distance from the sun, farther from it than we are when it is in opposition. But besides being placed at so much greater distance from it, we have in this situation the bright sun excluding the planet from our view. It will be readily seen, therefore, why the superior planets are in so much better position for us to see them in opposition than at conjunction.

From conjunction to opposition the planet is west of the sun, and will be below the horizon at sunset, and will rise some time during the night. At first it will appear just before sunrise as a morning star, but will gradually rise earlier each night until, when it reaches opposition again, it will rise just as the sun sets. Half-way between conjunction and opposition it is again at quadrature.

From opposition to conjunction the planet will be east of the sun and above the horizon at sunset. When a planet is in conjunction with the sun, it passes the meridian, or the point half-way between rising and setting, about noon, and is above the horizon with the sun during the day. When it is in opposition it passes the meridian about midnight, and is above the horizon during the night. When it is at quadrature and moving toward conjunction, it passes the meridian about six o'clock in the evening, and may be seen in the western half of the sky during the early evening, and will set before midnight. When it is at quadrature and moving toward opposition, it will rise some time between midnight and sunset, and will be in view in the east during a part of the first half of the night. The nearer it is to opposition, the earlier in the evening it rises and the longer it may be seen.

The main movement of the superior planets among the stars is from west to east, and this is known as their direct motion. But not far from opposition they seem to hesitate, then move more slowly, then finally stop, remain stationary for a time, turn back on their tracks, and start off in the opposite direction. This is their retrograde motion. They do not continue in it as long as in the direct motion; but after a comparatively short time they again hesitate, go more slowly, stop, remain stationary, then turn back and swing off in the original direction, and continue to move in this direction until they are again approaching opposition. It is exactly in the middle of this sweep toward the west that the planet is in opposition. Close observation will show that the superior planets also make something of the same sort of a loop in their path among the stars that the inferior planets make, and for the same reason. The only difference is that when a superior planet is retrograding we are passing it, and when an inferior planet retrogrades it is passing us.

In giving this rather rough outline of the way the planets in general move among the stars, reaching in their wanderings these various positions with relation to the sun and the earth, the intention is only to fix some definite situations from which to consider the movements of the individual planets. When we come to know each planet as an individual, and to follow it as it comes and goes in the heavens, and to watch its ever-wonderful changes in brilliancy, these situations will have a much more definite meaning to us and a relatively greater interest and importance. The planets as they appear to us all move along pretty much the same path; but each has its own way of gracing this path, and each its particular manner of changing in aspect.

IX

THE PATH OF THE PLANETS

Though the planets are called wanderers, they are not by any means the vagrants that the name might imply. They have a fixed course among the stars from which they never deviate, and the ways of all of them, and also of the sun and the moon, are confined to a comparatively narrow strip in the sky.

That strip is called the zodiac. It is only sixteen degrees wide, and extends like a narrow band all the way around the heavens. It lies so that it is always easy to observe; and, being so limited, very little observation is necessary to become familiar with every part of it. Within its limits all the movements of the sun, the moon, and the planets take place. Through the center of it is the ecliptic, the great circle that marks the annual apparent path of the sun through the heavens. It is the standard circle from which we measure the paths of the moon and the planets. Whatever degree their courses vary from the ecliptic is what we call the inclination of their orbits. If the plane of the orbit of a planet is tilted away from the ecliptic, the planet will travel half the time on one side of it, and half the time on the other.

The orbits are, in fact, very little inclined to the ecliptic, and all but one of the planets may always be found within three degrees of it, most of them nearer than this. The one exception is Mercury, which is sometimes as much as seven degrees from this central line of the zodiac, but ordinarily it is not so far as this. Uranus is so nearly on the ecliptic that an ordinary observer would not notice the deviation, and particularly as Uranus can rarely be detected with the naked eye, and can never be thus followed. Of the four planets which are the ones we ordinarily see, Mars and Jupiter are never as much as two degrees from the ecliptic, Saturn never more than two and a half degrees, and Venus never more than about three degrees. They are all usually nearer than these outside limits. The greatest distance of the moon from the ecliptic is about one and a half degrees.

Hence, with the exception of Mercury, all the planets and the sun and the moon travel in a path six degrees wide, which is only one degree wider than the distance between the pointers as we see them in the Great Dipper. The fact that the zodiac is sixteen degrees wide, or eight degrees on each side of the ecliptic, is due only to a very generous allowance for the vagaries of Mercury, which he really does not quite need. For Mercury is always as much as twice the breadth of the moon, or one degree, inside of the zodiac, and usually more than that.

Because the earth is tilted on its axis twenty-three and a half degrees from the perpendicular, the ecliptic runs through the heavens in an oblique circle, crossing the line of the equator at two points called the vernal and autumnal equinoxes. The equator in the heavens is the great circle extending around the celestial sphere half-way between the north and south poles. It is always practically ninety degrees from the north star, and the points at which the ecliptic intersects it are called the equinoxes. These are the only two points on the ecliptic that are just ninety degrees from the pole. The word equinox is derived from *equus* (equal) and *nox* (night), and when the sun is at the equinoxes the days and nights are of equal length.

From the vernal to the autumnal equinox the line of the ecliptic is north of the equator, and hence high in the sky, reaching its highest point midway between the equinoxes. It then crosses the equator again and runs obliquely south to the lowest point in its path, and then curves northerly back to the vernal equinox. The vernal equinox is the point at which the sun arrives when spring begins. This results in the sun's being north of the equator from spring until autumn, and south of it from autumn to spring.

As the part of the zodiac that we can see best at night is that opposite where the sun is, so in summer, when the sun is high, we see best the part of the zodiac which is low in the southern skies in the evening; and in the winter, when the sun is in the southern half of his journey, the part of the zodiac best seen by us is high in the heavens. No part of it, however, is ever as high as the zenith, or directly overhead, and no planet is ever seen as far north as the zenith in any place whose latitude is more than twenty-three and one-half degrees from the equator.

To know the paths of the planets it is necessary to know only twelve constellations out of the seventy or more in the entire heavens; but it is difficult to imagine any one's learning these twelve without becoming interested in and more or less acquainted with many of the splendid stars and constellations that lie on each side of them. The larger one's acquaintance is with the appearance of the skies as a whole, the easier, naturally, it will be to distinguish the planets from the stars, and to follow their courses. But the planets themselves may be intimately known quite apart from any but the twelve constellations forming the zodiac. Happily, among them we shall find some of the most beautiful constellations in the heavens, and some of the most splendidly brilliant first-magnitude stars.[1]

The twelve constellations of the zodiac are as follows:

Pisces, the Fishes.
Aries, the Ram.
Taurus, the Bull.
Gemini, the Twins.
Cancer, the Crab.
Leo, the Lion.
Virgo, the Virgin.
Libra, the Scales or Balance.
Scorpio, the Scorpion.
Sagittarius, the Archer.
Capricornus, the Goat.
Aquarius, the Water-Carrier.

We shall begin at the point of the vernal equinox to trace the line of the ecliptic through these constellations, and that line will mark for us the path of the sun, the moon, and all the planets. It is convenient to begin at this point, because it is where the sun crosses the equator in the spring, and hence it is at the beginning of that part of the ecliptic which lies north of the equator.

The point of the vernal equinox is now situated in the constellation Pisces. It is not marked by any bright star, but is not very difficult to find. It marks the point on the eastern horizon where the sun rises about March 21st, and about the 21st of September it is on the eastern horizon exactly opposite that point in the western sky where the sun sets. It is always ninety degrees from the pole, and if one chances to know the constellation Cassiopeia, which is shaped like a chair and is on the opposite side of the pole from the Big Dipper, one can locate the vernal equinox by drawing a line from the pole-star through the star which marks the lower part of the front of the chair, and extending it until it is ninety degrees long. The ninety degrees can be estimated by using the distance between the pointers in the Dipper (which is five degrees) as a measure. The star mentioned in Cassiopeia is about thirty-two degrees from the north star.

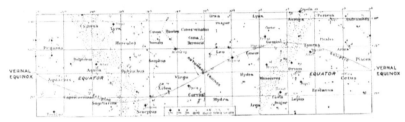

MAP SHOWING THE CONSTELLATIONS OF THE ZODIAC AND THE LINE OF THE ECLIPTIC
RUNNING THROUGH THEM

The paths of all the planets, save one, lie always within three degrees of the ecliptic.

Having once learned the constellations of the zodiac and, approximately, the line of the ecliptic, it is not necessary for the ordinary observer to keep in mind the exact location of the vernal equinox. It is, however, an important point for the student of mathematical astronomy.

Beginning at this point, the ecliptic runs through Pisces in a northeasterly direction for about thirty degrees to Aries, the second constellation of the zodiac.

ARIES

Aries is best seen in the autumn when the sun is in the opposite side of the heavens. It is marked by a small acute-angled triangle, with the apex toward the north and the brightest star of the three at the apex. This star is called Hamal, and, while not a first-magnitude star, is a rather bright one of the second magnitude; and the triangle itself is very distinctly marked. It is the only group of stars by which to distinguish Aries, and it is sometimes confused with the little constellation called Triangulum, which lies just west of it, or above it, as it rises. With this in mind, Triangulum may be made to serve as an identifying mark. They both rise just a trifle north of the exact east early in the evenings of late September and October. Triangulum rises first, with its apex toward the south. In less than an hour the triangle of Aries arrives with its apex pointed north. The ecliptic runs about five degrees below this triangle, and its path across Aries is about twenty-eight degrees long. When one sees any very bright star in Aries, one may be sure it is a planet. The sun is in Aries from April 16th to May 13th.

During the summer this constellation is not visible in the early evening; but it may be seen every evening from September to April, drawing all the time nearer to the sun, and setting earlier each evening until the sun blots it out.

37

From this constellation the ecliptic runs into Taurus, the third zodiacal constellation.

TAURUS

This constellation may be identified by the brilliant first-magnitude star Aldebaran,2 and the misty Little Dipper of the Pleiades. It is a very beautiful and large constellation. About an hour and a half after the triangle of Aries has risen, the soft-twinkling cluster of tiny stars which form the Pleiades comes above the eastern horizon, and about an hour later a V-shaped cluster of brighter stars, with a very bright-red one at the end of the lower half of the V, appears. This last cluster is the Hyades, and the bright star is Aldebaran.

By these two clusters we may know the constellation. The ecliptic passes across Taurus about four degrees east of the Pleiades, and about seven degrees west of Aldebaran. The planets in passing through this region often come very close to the Pleiades, and parts of the group are sometimes occulted by the moon. Taurus is conspicuous in the eastern evening sky from September until nearly January. From that time on until May it may be seen in the evening, high up in the sky, a little farther west each evening, until it disappears in May. Among the four planets that we most see Mars is the only one that resembles Aldebaran in color. They are both reddish, but Mars is always west of Aldebaran near the line of the ecliptic, and also it does not have the same twinkling face that Aldebaran shows; hence the star and the planet need never be confused. Mercury, it is true, is reddish and twinkles, but so seldom needs to be taken into account that it will not be troublesome. The other planets when in Taurus will proclaim themselves by their color and size. There is no very bright star in Taurus except Aldebaran, which has been described. Any bright star north of it in the constellation is sure to be a planet.

Through Taurus the line of the ecliptic runs in a northeasterly direction, and about fifteen degrees east from Aldebaran it passes about half-way between two fairly bright stars which mark the tips of the horns of Taurus, and from there on into the fourth constellation.

GEMINI

Gemini lies northeast of Taurus, and is outlined by a box-shaped figure something more than twenty degrees long and about five degrees wide. The two stars marking the end of it farthest from Taurus are the famous twins,

Castor and Pollux.<u>3</u> Pollux is a first-magnitude star, and Castor is very little less bright. They are both very charming stars, and too conspicuous to escape easy identification. Castor is greenish in tint, and rises between an hour and a half and two hours later than Aldebaran. About fifteen minutes after he appears, Pollux, with a yellow-tinted face, comes up over the eastern horizon. They rise about thirty degrees north of the exact east. The ecliptic has reached its highest point north just after passing through the horns of Taurus. It then runs through Gemini in a southeasterly direction, curving diagonally across the main figure and passing five or six degrees below Pollux. Gemini can be seen from October to early June. It is particularly charming in May in the northwest just after sundown, and when any of the planets are going along this part of their path at that season, they are sure to win one's interest and admiration.

CANCER

After leaving Gemini the ecliptic passes through the small constellation Cancer. Its way runs southeasterly for about twenty degrees, passing just south of a charming little cluster of stars which can be dimly seen with the unaided eye, but comes out brilliantly with an opera-glass. It is called Præsepe, or the Bee-hive, and is the only object to attract attention in Cancer. Fortunately, it is so situated as to mark the line of the ecliptic through the constellation. The Bee-hive rests almost exactly on the ecliptic.

LEO

Leaving Cancer, the sun enters Leo, a large, well-marked constellation known to many persons by the conspicuous figure in it of a sickle. At the end of the handle of the Sickle is Regulus, one of the bright first-magnitude stars. A little more than fifteen degrees east of the Sickle the rest of the constellation is marked by a large triangle formed by three rather bright stars. Both of these figures are well marked and easily seen, making Leo one of the easiest of the constellations to find. The sun crosses it in a southeasterly direction which leads straight across Regulus. The star is often occulted by the moon, and by the sun also, though that we cannot see on account of the blinding light of the sun.

Leo is visible nearly eight months in the year. It is in the eastern sky early in the evening in the winter, and shines all night from late in December until

April. In May and June it is traveling westerly, but high up in the sky. In July it is in the western sky in the evening. The sun passes through it from August 7th to September 14th. Regulus is a white star, and twinkles violently, so that it is easily distinguished from any planet that is passing near it. In the other part of the constellation the path of the planets runs about ten degrees below the triangle.

VIRGO

When the sun has passed Leo it enters the largest of all the constellations, Virgo, and passes through it in forty-five days, from September 14th to October 29th. The constellation is far from rich in bright stars; but one may find the ecliptic, or path of the sun, by following a curved southeasterly line from Regulus about sixty-five degrees until it reaches Spica,4 a very bright first-magnitude star in this comparatively starless region. If there is any doubt about Spica, it may be found by following the curve of the handle of the Big Dipper about thirty degrees, which brings one to the splendid Arcturus, and then about thirty degrees farther on, which points one to Spica.

Eight or nine days after entering Virgo the sun crosses the equator at the autumnal equinox, and the rest of the ecliptic lies farther south. Spica is about ten degrees south of the equator.

Spica is in the east during the early evenings in April and May; throughout June and July it may be seen in the south during the evening. In October it sets at about the same time as the sun.

The autumnal equinox, or the point where the ecliptic crosses to the south of the equator, is in Virgo, and lies about fifteen degrees northeast of Spica.

LIBRA

Libra is the next zodiacal constellation, and it is a small one. The sun passes through it in about twenty-three days. It may be known by four fairly bright stars which form a more or less imperfect square. The ecliptic passes along the southern edge of this figure.

During the summer and early autumn, Libra is best seen. It is then passing across the southern sky, drawing nearer the west each evening. A planet passing across this constellation would always be easy to identify, since it would always be so much brighter than any star in this region. The sun enters

Libra about October 29th, and it is not visible in the evening during the rest of the year.

SCORPIO

It is a joy to know Scorpio, quite aside from its connection with the path of the planets. It is a brilliant constellation, best seen during the summer and autumn, as it passes across the southern sky. It is the most southerly of any of the constellations of the zodiac; but the ecliptic passes through only a very small portion of the northern part of it, so the sun does not reach the most southerly point in its path while it is in this constellation.

Scorpio may be best identified by its brilliant deep-red star Antares,5 which is supposed to lie in the heart of the Scorpion. The whole figure makes a splendid serpent-like sweep toward the southern horizon, and is one of the most conspicuous objects just west of the Milky Way in the south in summer.

The line of the ecliptic runs about three degrees north of Antares; hence the planets in their course sometimes pass very near it. Jupiter has been in that region all this year (1912), and will not be far from there the early part of 1913. Mercury and Mars both have something the color of Antares; but this is not likely to result in any confusion. The star is always there, and in the same relative situation with reference to the other stars. When Mars is there, it will always be above the star. Mercury can seldom be seen when he is in Scorpio. If he is in greatest elongation while there, he will still be near the sun, and the sun, as seen from the middle latitudes, is so far south and so near the horizon when in that part of the ecliptic that the situation will not be favorable for seeing the planet. Farther south, and particularly in high altitudes, Mercury could be well seen in Scorpio, but if the position of Antares is kept in mind, Mercury will easily be recognized as a stranger in the constellation.

The sun enters Scorpio about November 21st, and the constellation then ceases to be visible in the evening sky until the following May. It is in its greatest glory during the summer and early autumn.

SAGITTARIUS

When the sun leaves Scorpio it crosses the Milky Way into Sagittarius, and there reaches the lowest point in its path, twenty-three and one-half degrees south of the equator. This constellation is best distinguished by the little "milk dipper," which is easily seen turned upside down just at the eastern edge of the Milky Way. The line of the ecliptic runs a little north of it. The constellation may be best seen during about the same months that Scorpio is visible. The sun enters it, and it passes out of view about the middle of December.

CAPRICORNUS AND AQUARIUS

From Sagittarius the ecliptic runs in a northeasterly direction through a region in which there are no very bright stars, nor any very distinct outlines of figures. The two constellations through which it passes are Capricornus and Aquarius. It then runs a few degrees into Pisces, and there reaches the vernal equinox, where we began to trace its course.

Although one cannot trace the line of the ecliptic with the same definiteness in this region as in one where there are bright stars to mark the way, yet when a planet is in this part of its path it is perhaps more conspicuous and more easily recognized than when it appears in any other part of the sky, because of the very absence of other bright bodies. These constellations comprise all that region running from the Milky Way east to the vernal equinox. It is a part of the heavens easily seen during the pleasant evenings of summer and autumn, and if a planet is crossing it during those seasons it is particularly well placed for observation.

The two brightest stars in Capricornus are of the third magnitude, and lie about twenty degrees northeast of the "milk dipper." The ecliptic runs just under them. Through Aquarius it runs six or seven degrees above a waving line of faint stars, which are supposed to represent the water that Aquarius is pouring from his urn.

If one will take the trouble to trace the line of the ecliptic through the sky, and remember that it lies exactly in the center of the zodiac, and that the planets are, therefore, within a very few degrees of it, one will have no trouble in keeping track of them. The mere knowing of these constellations is in most cases sufficient, since the planets will disclose their identity in other ways than by position merely.

The *signs* of the zodiac are somewhat different from the constellations. They are simply twelve equal divisions of thirty degrees each, making in all three hundred and sixty degrees, which is the whole number of degrees in any circle. They are so divided for convenience in scientific observation and reckoning. About two thousand years ago the signs and the constellations in the main coincided, and they still bear the same names. The point of the vernal equinox was then at the beginning of the sign and the constellation Aries. But, owing to certain motions of the earth, this point shifts backward, or toward the west, about one degree every seventy-two years. In two thousand years it has shifted about twenty-eight degrees, until now the sign Aries, with the vernal equinox at its western boundary, lies almost wholly in the constellation Pisces, the sign Taurus corresponds approximately to the constellation Aries, and so on around the circle. It is important to know this in following the planets, because all almanacs and scientific publications deal mainly with the *signs* of the zodiac, and not with the *constellations*. When a planet's place is said to be in Aries, Taurus, or Gemini, one will find it in Pisces, Aries, or Taurus, respectively. And so it is with all the other signs; they are each one constellation behind the one bearing the same name. And this is why, beginning with the vernal equinox, Pisces is the first constellation in the zodiac, while Aries is the first sign.

The following is a list of the signs of the zodiac, with the corresponding constellations. The symbols given in parenthesis are the ones used for these signs in all almanacs:

	SIGN		CONSTELLATION
Spring signs	Aries	(♈)	Pisces
	Taurus	(♉)	Aries
	Gemini	(♊)	Taurus
Summer signs	Cancer	(♋)	Gemini
	Leo	(♌)	Cancer
	Virgo	(♍)	Leo
Autumn signs	Libra	(♎)	Virgo
	Scorpio	(♏)	Libra
	Sagittarius	(♐)	Scorpio
Winter signs	Capricornus	(♑)	Sagittarius
	Aquarius	(♒)	Capricornus
	Pisces	(♓)	Aquarius6

44

X

MERCURY

While Mercury is one of the five planets that can be seen with the naked eye, it must be confessed that he does not play any important part in the great spectacle of nature as we see it in the skies. But in a certain way this only adds to our interest in him. The very rarity of his appearances and the difficulty of finding him give a zest to the search, and a sense of achievement, when it is successful, that one does not have with regard to the other planets. It is something akin to the feeling one has when, after a long tramp to some secluded recess in the woods in search of the shy pink lady's slipper, a splendid specimen of that lovely flower suddenly comes into view hanging gaily on its stalk, ready for the use of whatever fairy foot may tread its shady groves.

Then, too, the spring o' the year is the most likely time to see Mercury in the evening sky. He comes into his best position for this view of him just when the evenings are growing longer and milder and one begins to hunger for outdoor things, so that the quest of him at that time has the gladness that goes with our first excursions into the open after a winter's housing, whether it be in search of flowers, or birds, or stars, or simply the general loveliness of everything that belongs to the beginning of the outdoor season.

The reason Mercury is so elusive is that he is always very near the sun, and in consequence his light is dimmed by the brighter light shed by that luminary until it is well below the horizon; and after the sun has set, the planet is so involved in the usual haziness of the atmosphere near the horizon that the conditions must be very favorable in order to see him. Though there are recorded observations of Mercury as far back as nearly three hundred years before Christ, yet some of the older of the modern astronomers, before the days of the perfected telescope, are said not to have seen him at all; and the most important observations of the planet nowadays are made in broad daylight, when it is higher up in the skies and free from the mists of the horizon. This can be done by means of a powerful telescope, because it is possible in this way to shut off the light of surrounding bodies; but, of course, the conditions are not as favorable as if midnight observations could be made. Still, if one knows just when and where to look, Mercury can be seen with the naked eye at least once or twice a year, and sometimes oftener than this, especially if one chances to live in one of the Western States, where the air is very clear and the situation in latitude and altitude more favorable than, say, in New England, or in the middle Atlantic States. In our Northern States, and in the whole of England, this planet is more difficult to see, because of the longer twilight in northern latitudes, and also because the line of the ecliptic, over which it passes, seems there lower down in the skies, while in the far South, say in Cuba or Porto Rico, the twilight is shorter, the ecliptic runs high in the sky, and the situation is favorable for a good view even though the atmosphere is no clearer than it is farther north.

WHEN AND WHERE TO FIND MERCURY

Mercury is never more than twenty-eight degrees from the sun, and is brightest when the distance between them is somewhere near twenty-two degrees, or about four times the distance between the pointers, in the Big Dipper. The direction in which to search for him must always be along the line of the ecliptic obliquely above the sun. Since his orbit is inclined seven degrees to the ecliptic, he will be some place within seven degrees of this line, on one side or the other. Within this narrow strip in the sky, fourteen degrees wide and twenty-eight degrees long, Mercury will be found whenever he is visible at all. And this strip may be further shortened by at least twelve degrees; for when the planet is nearer than that to the sun it is futile to attempt to see him with the naked eye, save in very exceptional conditions. The five degrees between the pointers will serve as an aid in measuring these distances.

We can never see Mercury with the naked eye except when he is near one elongation or the other; and even then he is visible only about an hour after the sun is down in the evening or about an hour before it rises in the morning. Three times each year he appears in the evening for more or less than a week, according to the situation of the observer, and three times a year he is visible in the morning for about the same length of time. But, owing to his position with relation to us, the evening exhibit that comes in the spring is the most favorable one for a good view of him, and the morning appearance that is most favorable is the one that comes in the autumn.

The mean synodic period of Mercury is about one hundred and sixteen days, or a little less than four months. That is, he returns to greatest eastern elongation and can be seen in the evening sky about every one hundred and sixteen days, and the same length of time elapses between his appearances in the morning sky at greatest western elongation. But this mean synodic period is made up of synodic periods varying in different revolutions from one hundred and five to one hundred and thirty-four days. So, though one may mark the dates at which the various positions of the planet occurred during any one revolution, one cannot so easily determine the exact time at which he will be found in the same positions at the next revolution; that is, whether the revolution will take place in less or more than one hundred and sixteen days. The earth and the planet are each traveling at varying rates of speed, according as they are near the sun or farther from it, and obviously it is a situation that requires careful mathematical work to compute. The almanac must be referred to for the exact date.

But, lacking an almanac, one will generally find that Mercury will return to the same position relative to the earth and the sun within a few days of his mean synodic period. Three periods, however much they may vary individually, are almost always equal to three hundred and forty-eight days, or three times the mean period. This is seventeen days less than a year. Hence, if one is lucky enough to have seen Mercury at eastern elongation one spring, and will look the next year about seventeen days earlier, the planet will be found a little to the east (about fifteen degrees) of where he was when first seen the year before. He is there in the same position with relation to us and the sun that he had the preceding spring, but in a slightly different relation to us and the stars, because the sun lacks seventeen days of having completed its apparent yearly journey around the zodiac. It must still go through about one half of a constellation.

When Mercury shows himself at eastern elongation, he may be seen in the west as an evening star for somewhere near a week, each evening drawing nearer to the sun. When he disappears from view he passes between us and the sun, and about four weeks later appears in the morning sky before the sun rises. Under favorable conditions he is again visible for a week or more; and then, again approaching the sun, he can be seen no more for about ten weeks, during which time he passes through superior conjunction on the other side of the sun from us and comes back to eastern elongation.

Thus we can get, under very favorable conditions, six short views of Mercury during the year—three in the evening and three in the morning. So many views, however, are rarely secured by any but the professional observer. The circumstances may well be considered felicitous if one succeeds in getting a glimpse of him once or twice a year—at his favorable situation in the evening in the spring and the morning in the autumn. The sight of him, though, is truly worth a little inconvenience—even to the extent of facing a cold evening wind in the very early spring or getting out of a comfortable bed before dawn during the first cool mornings of autumn.

It is hardly possible to say exactly where one can find Mercury at all times during a long succession of revolutions. Moreover, it is not necessary. These computations are made anew each year by experts in the employ of the government, and the result is published in the *Nautical Almanac*. From there it finds its way into all almanacs, so it is easy of access to any one.

In the almanacs Mercury is represented by the sign (☿). It is a conventionalized form of the caduceus, or wand, carried by the god Mercury as a symbol of his power.

The next seven eastern and western elongations of Mercury occurring after the publication of this book are as follows:

Eastern Elongation (Evening Star).	Western Elongation (Morning Star).
18 November, 1912.	27 December, 1912.
10 March, 1913. (Favorable for viewing.)	24 April, 1913.
7 July, 1913.	22 August, 1913. (Favorable for viewing.)
1 November, 1913.	10 December, 1913.
22 February, 1914. (Favorable for viewing.)	6 April, 1914.
18 June, 1914.	5 August, 1914. (Favorable for viewing.)
15 October, 1914.	23 November, 1914.

DISTANCE AND BRIGHTNESS

Of all the planets Mercury is nearest the sun. His average distance is thirty-six million miles. He is nearly eighty times nearer than Neptune, the outermost planet, and more than two and one-half times nearer than we are. But his orbit departs so far from being a circle that his distance from the sun varies as much as fifteen million miles. When he is nearest the sun, or in perihelion, he is only twenty-eight million miles from it; when he is farthest, or in aphelion, his distance is forty-three million miles. There is even greater variation in his distance from us. The difference between his least possible and his greatest possible distance from us is as much as eighty-nine millions of miles. For the earth has an elliptical orbit as well as Mercury, and when we are at perihelion, which occurs in the winter, we are three millions of miles nearer to the sun than we are in mid-summer. If Mercury chances to be then at his greatest distance from the sun, and also at inferior conjunction, or between us and the sun, he is only forty-seven millions of miles from us. If, when we are farthest from the sun, he also is at his greatest distance from it, and is in superior conjunction, or on the other side of the sun from us, he is one hundred and thirty-six millions of miles from us.

These changes in distance from the earth have much to do with Mercury's changes in apparent brightness to us. At his brightest, when he appears at greatest elongation and we can see him without a telescope, he is brighter than Arcturus, the brilliant first-magnitude star in Boötes, that swings over us nightly from early spring to late autumn. When seen with the naked eye, he is also red in color, somewhat like Arcturus; but through a telescope he is dull silver, like the moon, or even more ashy in his paleness. As he goes farther and farther from us he becomes dimmer and dimmer and can be followed only with a telescope until, even with this aid to vision, he is lost in the rays of the sun at superior conjunction. His apparent diameter as mathematically measured varies from five seconds, when he is farthest away, to thirteen seconds, when he is nearest.

When he is at his nearest possible distance from us, light travels from Mercury to us in a little more than four minutes. At his greatest possible distance we could not receive the waves of light that he sends out in less than twelve minutes. As a matter of fact, we do not receive them at all, for, as we have seen, he is invisible when at his greatest possible distance from us, being then on the far side of the sun.

Another cause of Mercury's apparent change in brightness is due to the fact that, in common with Venus, he goes through phases from crescent to full like the moon. This is, as we have seen, a result of his shining only by reflected light and of his orbit's being between ours and the sun. If he shone by his own light, he would be at his nearest approach to us a very brilliant body indeed. As it is, his dark side is turned toward us when he is nearest, and when his full face is illuminated he is on the far side of the sun. We see half of his face when he is at greatest elongation; but he is brightest when we see less than half, because he is then nearer to us, and the difference in distance more than compensates for the difference in illumination.

These phases cannot be seen with the naked eye, but it requires only a small telescope to show them, and a very charming little moon-like body Mercury is when we see them. His horns point toward the east when he is coming toward us and nearing inferior conjunction, and when he is backing away from us and going toward greatest western elongation they point toward the west. It was through the blunting of one of these horns when the planet was in certain positions that a mountainous surface was suspected, so great is the significance of small details in observations.

As a mere place from which to view the other bright bodies Mercury would be far superior to the earth. He not only has the sun nearly seven times larger in appearance at its mean distance than we see it, but, being himself nearest the sun, all the other planets are outer planets in relation to him, and all have their discs fully illuminated.

The earth and the moon, as seen from Mercury, would show as a splendid pair of stars circling about each other, the earth more brilliant than any first-magnitude star, and the moon of the third magnitude, or about as bright as Phecda, the star at the bottom of the bowl of the Big Dipper, just under the beginning of the handle. The earth would show a disc of about twenty seconds, and the moon one of about eight seconds, with a distance between them of about 871 seconds. Some idea of what this distance is may be had if one knows Mizar, the star at the bend of the handle of the Dipper, and its tiny shining attendant, Alcor. These two stars are 708 seconds apart. The distance between them is about equal to one-third of the diameter of the moon as measured from the earth. It does not appear to be nearly so much as that, and some persons have difficulty in separating the two stars; but the moon is not only inconstant but deceptive, and owing to its brilliancy seems always proportionately larger than it really measures.

Venus would appear from Mercury as much as four times as large as she seems to us—a veritable little moon, and always full, her size varying slightly as Mercury speeded back and forth from the farthest to the nearest point in his orbit, changing the extreme of the distance between them from one hundred and ten million to less than twenty-four million miles. If Mercury needed a moon, he could well find some consolation for his lack of it in the presence of the lovely Venus in his sky.

MERCURY'S SIZE AND THE CONSEQUENCES OF IT

Mercury is the smallest of all the major planets. His diameter is about three thousand miles. It is only about nine hundred miles greater than that of our moon. The surface of Mercury is only one-seventh that of the earth, and his volume only one-twentieth. Jupiter and Saturn each have a satellite that is considerably larger.

Mercury would make a splendid satellite or a giant asteroid, but as a planet seems hardly to have had a fair chance in life. For being a small planet means something more than being constructed on smaller lines than some others are. It means a difference in physical development. It means less power to hold the gases that compose an atmosphere, which is the cover that shields the planets from the too burning rays of the sun and keeps their internal heat from radiating too quickly into space. It means less power to resist the tidal friction that the parent body uses as a brake to retard rotation. It means a shorter time of activity in life, and a long, dull, monotonous old age.

The nucleus that was detached from the great spiral, or the portion of nebula that was separated in whatever way from the parent body, to form Mercury chanced to be a small one. Being small, it was unable to add materially to its mass by attracting other particles to it through the power of gravitation, as a larger planet might do, and thus Mercury was doomed to develop with the limitations that nature's law has decreed as inevitable in the small bodies of our solar system, be they planets, satellites, or asteroids. Of these limitations the first and most far-reaching in its effect is the feebleness of its force of gravity, or power to attract other bodies.

Mercury's force of gravity is small. It is smaller than that of any of the other planets. It is a little less than one-quarter that of the earth. The same weight of feathers that would compose a pillow here would make a whole feather bed on Mercury. Any object weighing one hundred pounds here would weigh only twenty-four there. The materials composing our earth and all the planets are held together only by the force of gravity. The air we breathe would dart off into space with almost incredible fleetness if the earth had not sufficient gravitative force to hold it. Its particles are struggling all the time to get beyond this power. The lightest of them do get beyond it and are lost, and the less power we have to hold them the sooner they leave us. The greater the mass of a body, the rarer the gases it can hold in its atmosphere, for this mysterious force which pulls everything toward the center of a planet depends upon its mass, or the quantity of material in it. The planet may be very large because it is very much expanded. It may be gaseous even, and its mass would then be very small in proportion to that of a solid body of the same size. As it condenses, the particles draw closer and closer together, the density increases; but the mass is the same. It is only the size that diminishes.

So a planet with a small mass starts out in life with a disadvantage. It not only has little power to grow by drawing in particles from its environment, but also has little power to hold such as by their nature are volatile and swift of motion, as the molecules of gases are. The mass of Mercury is not exactly known. The only way we have of measuring the masses of the planets is by their influence through gravitation on other bodies near them. When a planet has satellites, the movements of the satellites tell the story, and by mathematical calculation the amount of material in the planet can be determined. But Mercury has no satellite, and the only way to determine his mass is by observation of his influence on Venus, and on an occasional comet which passes near enough to be disturbed by the planet. The particular comet which has been useful in determining the mass of Mercury is Encke's. On passing near the sun it comes sometimes near Mercury, and the pull it has repeatedly received from that little planet on such occasions is thought to be largely responsible for the comet's having become a part of the solar system. The changes in its orbit caused by these encounters show the power of Mercury, and hence the mass.

In these ways the mass of Mercury has been found, with reasonable belief in its accuracy, to be about three one-hundredths that of the earth. Yet there are, indeed, considerable differences regarding it among astronomers. The exact figures are not important to any but the close student. It is certain that the mass of Mercury is very small—so small that the planet probably never had much atmosphere, and almost undoubtedly has none to speak of now. The planet could not hold any molecule moving faster than two and forty-five one-hundredths miles a second, and few gases move as slowly as this. The proportion of light that Mercury reflects to that which he receives also points to a probable scarcity of atmosphere. If he had an atmosphere, it would have clouds. Clouds have a very high reflecting power, giving out about seventy-two per cent. of the light that falls upon them. Mercury reflects only fourteen per cent. of the light he receives, which shows at least a lack of clouds, and something more. It indicates a hard, dark, almost metallic surface, and a very considerable density. Density, however, is the only quality in the possession of which Mercury seems to occupy a middle ground among the planets, being slightly less dense than either Venus, or Mars, or the earth. The earth is the densest of all the planets, and it is about one-third more dense than Mercury. Density is simply the closeness with which the particles composing a body are packed together. A piece of gold, for example, is denser than a piece of iron of the same size.

WHAT THE SUN DOES FOR MERCURY

It is probable that Mercury has no alternations of light and darkness, causing day and night such as we know them. That is, the planet does not rotate on its axis in such a way as to turn first one side and then the other toward the sun as the earth does. In this, as in some other things, Mercury must accept the fate that overtakes many other small bodies which revolve around large ones —that of our moon, for instance, and the satellites of some of the other planets. Working under the law of gravitation, which gives such power to the large bodies, the sun has so retarded the rotation of Mercury that the planet now makes but one rotation on its axis during one circuit around that central body, and so keeps always the same face toward the sun. Some astronomers do not regard this as having been wholly proved; but all the later observations of Mercury strongly indicate that it is the fact, and it is coming to be more and more regarded as established.

But, even if this is the predicament into which Mercury has come, the planet is probably not in so bad a plight as many another body to which the same sort of thing has happened. The extreme eccentricity of his orbit, which has given him the true mercurial temperament, resulting in sprightliness, agility, and changeableness, is accountable for some mitigating circumstances. The sun may hold him so that he cannot turn his face away from that luminary; but it cannot keep him from rotating on his axis at a uniform rate of speed, and from this, combined with the vagaries caused by his eccentric orbit, come some interesting things.

Since Mercury is less than two-thirds as far from the sun at perihelion as he is at aphelion, there is a corresponding variation in his rate of speed. When he is nearest the sun, at perihelion, he darts along at the rate of thirty-five miles a second; at aphelion, when he is farthest from the sun, he travels only twenty-three miles a second. Twenty-three miles in one second is not exactly a snail's pace, terrestrially considered, and it is faster than the earth moves at any time; but the planet was named Mercury because of his swiftness, and we would not expect much lagging even when he is moving at his slowest gait. This difference in speed in different parts of his orbit causes what is called the librations of Mercury. When he is traveling at his swiftest pace he gets a little ahead of his rotation, the speed of which is uniform, and thus throws the sunlight somewhat farther around on one side. When his speed decreases, he falls behind his time of rotation, and thus gets a little more sunlight on the other side. Thus, during each revolution he juggles the sunlight a little farther around him than he could if he were a more steady-going planet.

These librations result in there being two strips on the surface of Mercury—one on each side—which undoubtedly have a day and night, varying in length in the different parts of the strips. The part that lies nearest the illuminated side of the planet has alternate periods of sunlight and darkness, each of considerable duration, while that part nearest the dark side has merely a glimmer of sunlight every eighty-eight days, which is Mercury's sidereal year, or the time required for him to make one revolution around the sun. These two strips on which the light varies comprise about one-eighth of the surface of Mercury. One half of his entire surface is always light, and of the other three-eighths are always dark. It is this dark, cold side that is turned toward us when Mercury is nearest to us.

It is possible that on those parts of Mercury where the sunlight and darkness are unstable there may be something resembling a tolerable temperature. They are something more than a thousand miles in breadth, and perhaps near the center of them the sun may give heat sufficient to enliven and yet not burn. More than likely, they are alternately scorched and frozen. For it takes more than the mere presence of sunlight to make a climate tolerable. Atmosphere is what is necessary, and we have seen that Mercury has probably lost practically all his atmosphere long, long ago. An atmosphere absorbs much of the radiant energy that comes from the sun before it reaches the more solid parts of a planet, and it also acts as a blanket in preventing the too rapid escape of such heat as the planet may have acquired. Thus it has the doubly beneficent office of tempering the rays that would otherwise be scorching and of hindering a radiation that would leave the planet stiffened and frozen.

Stiffened and frozen is what the dark side of Mercury undoubtedly is. The sun has never shone upon it since Mercury became a solid body. All the inherent heat it had has long since passed off into space, and its temperature must be somewhere near the absolute zero. The absolute zero is the point in temperature where all known substances become solid. It is more than 450° below the Fahrenheit zero, or more than 350° lower than any temperature recorded in our arctic regions—a degree of cold unthinkable to any but the scientist.

On the other side of Mercury the heat is beyond anything we have any notion of. With an equal atmosphere it would receive from the sun six thousand times as much light and heat as Neptune on an equal space, and, on an average, seven times as much as the earth. At Mercury's distance from the sun his hot side would be more than 300° above zero, if there were absolutely no atmospheric protection. Even though tempered by a thin atmosphere, as it may be, the heat on this side is still probably enough to boil away any water that might be there and to change some other substances from what we regard as their normal state.

Stability, at least, is a quality of the hot and the cold side of Mercury. Scorched and seared and desolate of life, as we know it, the one side lies under a blazing, dazzling sun. Cold and hard and bleak, and no less desolate, the other side turns its face toward the darkness of space. Thus they will remain until the end of time. And let us hope that, when the final catastrophe occurs and a new nebula is formed, the matter composing Mercury may find a place in a larger mass, and in its new incarnation have a fuller and larger life.

It is the atmosphere also which causes twilight, as well as the gradual changing from heat to cold. With no atmosphere, we would drop from full daylight to the darkness of starlight at the setting of the sun. So, with the thin air that Mercury probably has (if he has any), the two zones which are alternately light and dark, and hot and cold, are not much better off than the parts which are permanently either light or dark. They are plunged alternately from the temperature and light of the hot side of Mercury to the temperature of the cold side, with few gradations to prepare them for such extremes. Thus the only part of the planet that might be expected to have any variations of seasons fulfils the expectation with little satisfaction.

The only changes in climate which may have an appreciable effect are mainly those caused by the eccentricity of Mercury's orbit, which carries him so near the sun at certain times and so comparatively far away at others. When he is nearest the sun he receives more than twice as much heat and light as when he is farthest away. At aphelion he receives four times as much heat and light as the earth. At perihelion the amount of heat and light is increased to more than nine times that of the earth. Since it takes Mercury a little more than twelve weeks to make one revolution around the sun, he passes from nearest distance to farthest, or the reverse, every six weeks. And thus, as viewed from the planet, the sun expands gradually for six weeks until it has increased its diameter two and one-half times, and the next six weeks it diminishes in the same proportion. At such times, of course, the amount of heat is more or less according to the planet's distance from the sun; but all the time it is very great.

Moreover, it is believed that the axis on which Mercury rotates stands perpendicular to his orbit. This being the case, there would be on Mercury no change of seasons such as the earth has. The earth's axis is inclined a little more than twenty-three degrees to its orbit, and from this we get the sun's rays in a great variety of directions and different degrees of obliquity, causing the seasons, as we know them, in grateful variation. With the axis perpendicular, as it probably is in the case of Mercury, the sun's rays fall on the face of the planet always with the same degree of directness, the only relief from their greatest heat being when the planet backs away from the sun every six weeks, and when in his librations he turns first one sun-burned cheek and then the other toward the coolness of space.

Thus we must regard the smallest of our family of planets, Mercury, as always the dwarf among us, with never a fair chance to develop a rich and luscious life according to our ideas of such a life. Beaten by the sun's hard rays, and with no sufficient atmospheric protection; pulling always at his tether, but held firmly with his face to the center; circling at times with mercurial swiftness and thus cheating the sun into sending its rays farther toward the dark, cold side of him than it otherwise would, and with all his defects from a human point of view, we may still regard him as a right merry, roguish little planet, after all. He may be prematurely aged, he may have missed many experiences that the larger planets are having, he may have a long time to wait for the final change that will reunite us all; but he is not lying in sluggish inactivity until it comes.

In view of the fact that he is the only planet that twinkles, may it not suggest, when we see his ruddy face peering through the thick atmospheric mists near our horizon, that the impish little body is winking at us, and that it may be with planets as it is with people: they may not always be in an unfortunate plight because their fate is different from ours?

TRANSITS

Occasionally Mercury passes at inferior conjunction between us and the disc of the sun, appearing like a black spot against the sun, and thus makes what we call a transit. Because the planet is so small, his transit across the sun cannot be seen with the naked eye; but it is an interesting phenomenon to those who can view it with a telescope, though, apparently, astronomers do not regard it as having any great scientific importance. It is during a transit, however, that we watch for confirmation of the theories concerning Mercury's atmosphere, which, if it were a reality, would show a diffused light about the planet; and until this question is settled beyond any dispute it will always come up at the time of a transit of Mercury. At nearly every transit some observer sees these indications of an atmosphere; but the better the telescope, the less they seem to be seen. Hence it is probable that there is an illusion somewhere either of eye, or instrument, or mind, and that the majority opinion, which accords to Mercury practically no atmosphere, is about the correct one.

These transits occur at intervals of seven, thirteen, or forty-six years, according to the position of the earth. They would occur every time that Mercury passed inferior conjunction if the earth's orbit and that of Mercury were in exactly the same plane. But the orbit of Mercury, we have seen, is tilted out of the plane of the ecliptic, which marks our orbit, seven degrees, so that the only time the earth and the planet are anywhere nearly in the same plane is when they are at or near the points where their orbits cross each other.

The earth is near the two points where Mercury crosses the ecliptic about May 8th and November 9th, so that transits can occur only near these dates. Mercury passes these points four times every year, or once in each revolution around the sun. But the earth is not always there at the same time, and it is because of this that transits occur only in periods of seven, thirteen, or forty-six years. They occur more frequently in November than in May. The last transit was in November, 1907. The next will be on November 7, 1914, and there will not be another in November until 1927, an interval of thirteen years. But at the point where the May transits occur there will be one on May 7, 1924.

XI

VENUS

Of all the planets lovely Venus is the one that is best known and most admired. It far exceeds all the other planets in brilliancy and beauty when as an evening star it hangs in gracious silvery softness above the sun, which has just passed below the horizon; and it is not less surpassing in loveliness when as a morning star it comes into view shortly before the sun rises, its glowing face still silvery and bright, but yet tinged with the rosy flush of the eastern morning sky.

In either position it never twinkles as Mercury sometimes does, but shines so steadily and softly that at times its disc can almost be seen with the naked eye, and it has such brilliancy that its light can often be seen in the daytime, if one knows when and how to look for the planet. At its brightest it frequently throws a light sufficiently strong to cast a shadow, as one may easily prove by holding a book or some other opaque object between Venus and a white background, such as the wall of a white house. It is six times as bright as the brightest of all the fixed stars, Sirius, the beautiful dog-star, which we see in winter chasing across the southern skies after Orion.

Venus's superior brilliancy is due in part to the fact that it comes nearer to the earth than any other planet; but it is also intrinsically brighter than any of the others. From equal areas it reflects almost four times as much light as Mercury and three times as much as Mars.

WHEN AND WHERE TO SEE VENUS

When Venus appears in the sky she is not often mistaken for any other planet. Among all the planets she is the most readily recognized and the easiest to find. This is due largely to her extreme brilliancy and a peculiar silvery appearance that none of the other planets have; but also, in part, to her limited range in the sky, and her favorable situation for observation. Unlike Mercury, she is far enough away from the sun to be seen above the horizon for as much as three hours after sunset, and is then sufficiently high in the heavens to be seen free from the vapors of the atmosphere at the horizon. Yet, being one of the inferior planets, with her orbit smaller and nearer the sun than that of the earth, she can never get so far from the sun as to be at any uncomfortable height for viewing, and hence, when she can be seen at all, is always an obvious bit of brilliancy and a joy to the beholder. She is never higher in the sky than forty-five degrees, which is half-way between the horizon and the zenith, and is never farther away from the sun than forty-eight degrees. One frequently sees a bright planet higher up in the heavens than this; but it is never Venus nor Mercury.

We first begin to notice Venus in the evening sky about six weeks after she has passed superior conjunction. She is then very near the sun, and sets a little less than half an hour after sundown. Evening by evening she grows gradually brighter, mounts higher and higher in the sky and, consequently, sets correspondingly later, until in a little more than seven months after superior conjunction, and about six months after we have begun to watch her, she reaches her greatest elongation east from the sun. At that time she is usually somewhere near forty-five degrees above the sun, and is a very lovely and conspicuous object in the evening sky, setting a little more than three hours after sundown.

From this point she begins to travel back toward the sun, still becoming brighter each evening, because she is really coming nearer to us; and in about four or five weeks she attains the greatest brilliancy that she will have as an evening star during the particular revolution she is making. About twelve days after her brightest she will reach the point where she seems to be stationary for a time. This is when she is about to overtake us in our journey around the sun. After a short pause she will move on gradually, her course among the stars then being retrograde or westward; but what we most notice is that she is drawing nearer to the sun, setting earlier each evening, and becoming more and more difficult to see. At the end of about three weeks she is in inferior conjunction, on a line between us and the sun, and invisible. She has run her course as an evening star for nine and a half months, and has been visible anywhere from seven to eight months, the time of her invisibility depending upon the eye of the observer and the conditions of situation and atmosphere.

A week or two later we shall find her a splendid morning star, rising nearly an hour earlier than the sun. About three weeks thereafter she will be at her brightest as a morning star, and will continue to be very brilliant for some weeks. In about five more weeks she will have reached her greatest elongation west of the sun, and will rise about three hours and a half before dawn. Then she will begin to retrace her path, moving eastward, growing smaller all the time as she goes farther away from us, and showing a slower apparent movement, which gives one an agreeable sense of a reluctant parting, until after a little more than seven months she will have reached the sun and will again be in superior conjunction. She has then been a morning star for nine and a half months, and has been visible for about the same length of time that she was when she shone as an evening star.

This is a brief outline of a typical journey of Venus through one synodic revolution. She began one of these journeys on July 5, 1912, being then in superior conjunction. During the autumn of this year and the winter of 1912–13 she may be seen shining with great brilliancy in the west at sunset, and a few hours thereafter. Early in November, 1912, she and Jupiter will both be in Scorpio, where they will approach within two degrees of each other; and there is no doubt that their presence will add much charm to that region of the sky during the entire autumn.

About the middle of February, 1913, Venus will appear half-way up to the zenith at sunset. She will then be at her greatest distance east of the sun, and will be very bright; but, though a little nearer the sun, she will be still brighter shortly after the middle of March. A month later she will be invisible, and inferior conjunction will occur on April 24th. During most of May and all of June and July she will be a morning star, and her brilliant beauty will well repay an early morning outlook. She will get back to superior conjunction on February 11, 1914, and in that year she will be in an ideal situation for us to cultivate a more intimate acquaintance with her. From the latter part of March to November, 1914, she will be the brightest star in the western evening sky, and will do much to enhance the beauty of the pleasant summer evenings of that year. The sturdy, red-faced Mars will meet her on August 5th, a little more than a month before greatest eastern elongation, and might almost kiss her pale cheek as they pass within one-sixth of a degree of each other, a distance equal to less than one-third of the diameter of the moon.

The next long period when Venus will shine as an evening star will comprise the spring and early summer of 1916. She will be at her greatest distance from the sun during the last week of April, and will not pass from view until about the first of July. Then again she will be an evening star, and so seen in the west during the autumn of 1917 and the winter of 1917–18, reaching greatest eastern elongation during the first few days of December, 1917. Her next return to the evening sky will be for the first eight months of 1919, and the next will be for the winter of 1920–21 and the spring of 1921.

The synodic period of Venus is nearly five hundred and eighty-four days, or a little more than one year and seven months. That is, the planet returns to the same position with relation to the sun and the earth at intervals of about that length. The intervals do vary, however, as much as a week or more, owing to the various motions and situations of the planet and the earth. But every eight years Venus and the earth come around to almost exactly the same relative position with each other and the sun and the stars, and thus the appearances of Venus at the various seasons practically repeat themselves every eight years. The full splendor that she is to offer us in the summer of 1914 will be repeated in 1922, just as that of 1914 will but repeat that which she showed in 1906. And in each of the intervening years she will have again the same appearances that she had eight years before.

With the following table as a guide, the appearances of Venus can be followed through a number of years with sufficient accuracy for any but a close student of her movements. The exact dates of elongations and conjunctions will vary a few days, but for at least two or three multiples of eight years not enough to make any material difference in her various aspects.

1913—1921—1929—1937

Greatest eastern elongation, February 12th. Inferior conjunction, April 24th. Greatest western elongation, July 3d.

1914—1922—1930—1938

Superior conjunction, February 11th. Greatest eastern elongation, September 17th. Inferior conjunction, November 27th.

1915—1923—1931

Greatest western elongation, February 8th. Superior conjunction, September 14th.

1916—1924—1932

Greatest eastern elongation, April 26th. Inferior conjunction, July 5th. Greatest western elongation, September 14th.

1917—1925—1933

Superior conjunction, April 28th. Greatest eastern elongation, December 2d.

1918—1926—1934

Inferior conjunction, February 11th. Greatest eastern elongation, April 22d. Superior conjunction, November 25th.

1919—1927—1935

Greatest eastern elongation, July 6th. Inferior conjunction, September 14th. Greatest western elongation, November 25th.

1920—1928

Superior conjunction, July 5th.

The meetings of Venus with the other planets do not, however, occur with this delightful regularity. They all are moving about in their own ways, and engaged in their own affairs, and only the earth gets back to repeat the meeting with her in just eight years. These eight-year cycles are due to the fact that Venus makes thirteen revolutions around the sun while the earth makes eight. Her journey around the sun requires a little less than two hundred and twenty-five days (224.70), and the earth completes its revolution in a little more than three hundred and sixty-five days (365.25). So at the end of about two thousand nine hundred and twenty-two days—which equals eight years—they come into almost exactly the same relative positions in their orbits with which they started out, and begin the cycle anew.

DISTANCE AND BRILLIANCY

The mean distance of Venus from the sun is 67,269,000 miles. Her orbit more nearly approaches the form of a circle than that of any other planet. It is, like the orbits of the other planets, an ellipse, but of such small eccentricity that the difference between her greatest and least distance from the sun is scarcely more than a million miles. Light, traveling as it does, at the rate of a little more than one hundred and eighty-six thousand miles a second, goes from the sun to Venus in about six minutes. It takes something more than eight minutes for light-rays to come from the sun to us. When Venus is nearest the earth, her silvery beams come swiftly across to us in a little more than two minutes. When she is farthest from us, the rays of light require a few seconds more than fourteen minutes to travel over the distance. She is, when at her greatest distance, more than one hundred and thirty-five million miles farther from us than when at her nearest. This difference is due not to any great eccentricity in her orbit, or in that of the earth, such as causes Mercury's great variations of distance, but to the situation of the two bodies in their orbits: they are nearest together when they are on the same side of the sun, and farthest apart when on opposite sides.

Usually at inferior conjunction Venus is a little more than twenty-five million miles from the earth. At her nearest possible approach to us, however, which takes place at inferior conjunction, when the earth is nearest the sun and Venus is farthest from it, a situation which occurs only once or twice in a century, the distance between us and the planet is only a little more than twenty-three million miles. This is nearer than any other heavenly body ever approaches us, except the moon and, so far as we now know, one small asteroid. Also, it is nearer than Venus comes to any other heavenly body except perhaps Mercury. Her nearest approach to that planet is also about twenty-three million miles.

Unfortunately, our comparative proximity to this beautiful planet does not much aid us in learning anything about her personal peculiarities. Shining only by reflected light, and being, like Mercury, situated nearer to the sun than the earth is, when she comes around to the same side of the sun on which we are, her unillumined side is turned toward us, and at the point of very closest approach she is absolutely invisible to the naked eye. Through a telescope, however, she can be seen up to the very point of inferior conjunction. What we see then is a mere curved line of light, so thin is the crescent she presents; but it is always apparent except when the planet makes a transit. During a transit she is actually in our line of sight with the bright disc of the sun, and is neither above nor below it, as at the ordinary times of inferior conjunction. The slender crescent that we ordinarily see offers a very narrow field for observation.

If there is any one on Venus who is studying the earth, he has a much easier task than we have in our effort to learn something about her. The earth is not only somewhat larger than the planet, but when the two bodies are nearest together the disc of the earth is fully illuminated, and so must show a splendid face; and then, our atmosphere probably interferes less with close observation than that of Venus. This little terrestrial system would undoubtedly shine as a magnificent pair of stars if observed from Venus. At that distance our moon would appear considerably larger than Venus appears to us when at superior conjunction, the earth would seem much larger than Venus ever does to us, and the distance between them would seem to be a little more than the apparent diameter of the full moon as we see it. The light of the earth must cause much more of a shadow than we ever get from the light of Venus.

It has been suggested that light from the earth is responsible for a dusky illumination of the dark side of Venus, which is occasionally seen, and which enables us to distinguish her entire outline even when only the merest line of a crescent is really illuminated. It is known to be earth-shine that causes what is apparently the same phenomenon often seen by us on the moon; but it seems that there is no reason to think that our earth, at its distance, would be sufficiently brilliant to illuminate Venus even so slightly. The cause of the illumination is not known; but it is thought that it may have some electrical origin, probably similar to that of our aurora.

Venus has the same phases that Mercury has. She shows her full face when at superior conjunction, and is then farthest away and smallest to our view. As she moves toward us she first becomes gibbous, and then, at eastern elongation, like a half-moon. As she comes nearer to inferior conjunction, and hence nearer to us, she becomes a thinner and thinner crescent, and as she goes from inferior to superior conjunction these phases are repeated in reverse order. We see less than half of her face when she is at her greatest brilliancy, a phase which usually occurs when she is about forty degrees from the sun, as she is a few weeks before and after inferior conjunction. A very small glass will show the phases of Venus. They have occasionally been seen without artificial aid to vision by an exceptionally good eye. They were not known, however, until they were discovered by Galileo after the invention of the telescope in 1610.

THE LOVELY CRESCENT THAT VENUS SHOWS WHEN TO OUR VIEW SHE IS AT HER GREATEST BRILLIANCY

This remarkable photograph was made at the Yerkes Observatory by E. E. Barnard.

Venus would be many times brighter than she ever appears if the entire disc of the planet could be seen when it is nearest to us. The apparent diameter of the disc at that time is nearly seven times larger than when we see it at the planet's greatest distance from us. When Venus is in superior conjunction and farthest from the earth the disc measures only ten seconds, while at inferior conjunction its measure is nearly sixty-seven seconds. The diameter of the moon is about 1,868 seconds, so one could string across the diameter of the moon one hundred and eighty-six such planets as Venus appears to be when at her smallest, and only twenty-seven of the size that she appears to be when at her largest. Between these two extremes of size she changes gradually, day by day, from large to small and small to large, in ceaseless succession, as she approaches the earth and recedes from it in her orbital journey. Apparent diameter is determined by an actual measurement of the disc of a planet, and in the case of Venus indicates nothing as to brightness. When the apparent diameter is largest she is not visible to the naked eye.

RELATIVE APPARENT SIZE OF VENUS AT DIFFERENT PHASES OF ILLUMINATION

She shows the full disc when farthest away. As she draws nearer she shows first the half moon and then the smaller crescent. She is nearest when she shows the larger crescent. She is brightest, though, when she shows the smaller crescent.

VENUS'S LIKENESS TO THE EARTH

The fact that of all the planets Venus most resembles this good little earth on which our present lot is cast gives us a strong feeling of kinship with her, and a more lively interest in all her affairs than we might otherwise have. She and the earth are so nearly of one size that they are often referred to as twin sisters. There is a difference of less than three hundred miles in their diameters, the earth's diameter measuring 7,917 miles, and that of Venus 7,629 miles. The surface of the planet is about ninety-three per cent. as extensive as that of the earth; its mass is a little more than eighty per cent., and its volume about ninety per cent. as great as the earth's. Differing so little in these particulars, it follows that it must differ very little in density and gravity. The earth is the densest of all the planets, and Venus is only one-tenth less dense than the earth. Its force of gravity is not quite nine-tenths that of the earth. A removal from the earth to Venus would make just a comfortable reduction in one's weight. A person weighing one hundred and seventy-five pounds here would weigh on Venus one hundred and fifty-four. If through strength of appetite and weakness of will one should take on two hundred pounds of too, too solid flesh here, transportation to Venus would bring about an instantaneous reduction to a solid one hundred and seventy-six pounds—as much of a reduction as would be compatible with health.

Venus must have begun her career in much the same way that the earth began its career. The nebula that formed her nucleus was probably nearly the same size (contained about the same amount of matter) as that with which the earth began its existence. The two bodies have succeeded in capturing about the same amount of loose material, and their gravity is such that they can hold within their bounds particles traveling at about the same rate of speed. No molecule of gas coming within the range of Venus's attraction and traveling more slowly than six and thirty-seven hundredths miles per second can escape from Venus, and the earth can hold only such as move, when coming within its own attraction, with a less speed than six and ninety-five one-hundredths miles per second.

The earth has a moon, and Venus has none; but that may be because, like Mercury, Venus is too near the sun to be permitted to retain such a luxury. It is likely that if, in her earlier history, she had within the limit of her gravitative attraction the nucleus of a satellite, it would have been taken away from her by the stronger attraction of the sun. The same thing would have happened to us if we had been a little nearer the sun. And yet in 1645 a moon belonging to Venus was supposed to have been discovered, and it was thought to have been seen three times within the rest of that century, and four times within the first half of the following century. The last supposed view of it was in 1791; it has never been seen since. There is little doubt that it was an illusion of some kind. Perhaps, though, Venus has not the same need of a moon that we have.

ATMOSPHERE, DAY AND NIGHT, AND SEASONS

There is no doubt that Venus is in much better plight than Mercury, the other inferior planet, in regard to atmosphere. Until recently no one has questioned the belief that her atmosphere is very extensive—twice as heavy, perhaps, as that of the earth, dense, and full of clouds. The luminous ring about her, shown when she is making a transit across the face of the sun, points to a heavy atmosphere; and no less certain indications of it are given in the faint light which stretches beyond the termination of the horns when she is in the crescent phase, near inferior conjunction. Her very high reflecting power is also indicative of an atmosphere laden with clouds. White clouds form one of the most highly reflecting surfaces known, and the peculiar brilliancy of Venus is thought to be in great part due to the presence of large masses of clouds in her atmosphere. By the spectroscope, and in other ways, the water necessary to form clouds is shown to be abundant in her atmosphere. Even those astronomers who doubt the long-current belief in the large extent of her atmosphere concede an atmosphere of more or less density, though by one authority it is characterized as somewhat gauzy.

There is one vital point concerning the development of Venus upon which we have as yet no positive knowledge: the length of time in which she rotates on her axis. This is unfortunate, because until her time of rotation is known we cannot know much about her physical condition. Her rotation, we know, determines the length of her day and night, or whether, indeed, she has any. The time of it has been calculated to be anywhere from a little less than one of our days to two hundred and twenty-five, the latter being also the time of her revolution about the sun. Astronomers of equal reputation have come to exactly opposite results in their investigations. To one, the spectroscope has indicated the short day and night; to another it has shown no day and night, but a planet with one face forever toward the sun, like Mercury. What appeared to be stable surface markings have been observed, but have indicated under the eyes of different observers both the short day and no day at all. The disc has been measured during a transit, and shows so little flattening as to indicate a slow rotation and the long day. On the other hand, the best authorities think it unlikely that at the distance of Venus the sun could so retard the planet's rotation as to make it coincide with its time of revolution. Thus the question is still an open one.

The truth may be that, owing to the density of her atmosphere, the surface of Venus has never been seen at all, and that the apparently stable markings are but clouds more or less lacking in stability. The difficulty of observing Venus will probably make it impossible to determine this point by visual observation. It may some day be settled beyond a doubt by the spectroscope. In some way it will surely be settled. Astronomers have too often made possible what seemed to be impossible for us to doubt that some one will find a way to discover this secret of Venus. With them a failure to prove a conclusion does not mean to abandon the subject, but to try some other means of getting at the truth.

The sun viewed from Venus would appear considerably larger than it does to us. Its apparent diameter to us is a little more than thirty-two minutes, while on Venus it would be something more than thirty-eight minutes; that is, it would appear about one-fifth larger on Venus than it does to us. This is enough to make a material difference between the two planets in the amount of heat and light they receive. Venus receives nearly twice (1.9) as much heat and light from the sun as we receive, but less than one-third as much as Mercury. If she had no atmospheric protection, there is no question but that she would have a climate disastrously warm for a race of beings constituted as we are. The normal temperature of an unprotected body at the distance of Venus is about 158° Fahrenheit (70° Centigrade).

If Venus is finally proved to have no alternations of day and night, she is still better off than Mercury, who has practically no atmosphere to protect him from the intense heat of the sun. How much protection she has depends altogether on the extent of her atmosphere. It is probably not enough to make the hot side comfortable from our point of view; and Venus, being undoubtedly a solid body with no internal heat, the cold side must be cold beyond anything we have any conception of. But there may be a very considerable part on each side that, owing to the refraction of light by the atmosphere, is more or less well lighted, and is also more or less protected by this same beneficent atmosphere from deadly extremes of heat and cold. In this situation there would undoubtedly be lively currents of air from the heated side to the cooler; but even these may in some way carry with them some tempering effects on the climate, as we know such currents do here on the earth.

If it should prove that the length of the day and night on Venus is something near that of the earth's (and this seems not unlikely), she would then be indeed more like a twin sister to us. Being next to each other in our distances from the sun, and of nearly the same size, differing but little in density, mass, volume, and force of gravity, with her greater normal heat probably reduced by her heavier atmosphere to a temperature producing climatic conditions not very unlike ours, and with not very different alternations of day and night, we might well be considered more nearly related than any of the other members of the solar family.

The seasons, however, on Venus and the earth would not have much resemblance to each other. The axis of the earth is inclined to the ecliptic nearly twenty-three and one-half degrees, so that we receive the sun's rays with varying degrees of obliquity during our yearly journeying around it, which is the cause of our agreeable change of seasons. Venus travels with her axis so slightly inclined to her orbit (a little more than three degrees) that each particular parallel of latitude receives practically the same amount of sunlight every day in the year, though at different parallels the sun's rays strike with varying degrees of obliquity. However delightful or disagreeable the climate may be, there are no changes of seasons to speak of, and one could find variety only by going from place to place on the planet. She receives no compensation for this monotony by alternately receding from and approaching the sun as Mercury does, or by librations, such as he has. Her orbit being, as we have seen, so nearly circular as to permit of only small variations in her distance from the sun, and her axis so nearly perpendicular to her orbit, it follows that she has nothing to mark the year; and, whether she turns on her axis many times or only once during a revolution, life on Venus would be very monotonous to any one accustomed to our delightful variety of climate and seasons. Still, there is nothing in this monotony to prevent Venus from being a fairly comfortable habitation in some parts for such beings as inhabit the earth. The only real obstacle to habitability on Venus would be her lack of rotation and all that it involves.

Since we are not sure that we can see the surface of Venus, we cannot say what that surface is. Nevertheless, there is some reason to suspect that we would find there mountains of vast height. Certain irregularities have been observed at times, of a kind to indicate mountains covered with snow, extending beyond the clouds. They have been estimated to be many miles higher than any mountains we have on earth, their height depending somewhat upon the temperament of the observer. But inasmuch as these same high mountains have sometimes been thought to be only masses of clouds, it seems hardly safe to pronounce definitely upon them.

TRANSITS

On rare occasions, when Venus is in inferior conjunction, she makes a transit, and can then be seen as a black dot moving over the bright face of the sun. Transits can occur only when the earth and the planet are near the point where their orbits cross each other. The earth is at this point every year on June 7th and December 7th; but the orbit of Venus is such that she is there on the proper dates only four times in a period of two hundred and forty-three years. In every two hundred and forty-three years four transits take place. They occur in pairs, eight years apart, and in the same month. If a pair occur in June, it will be one hundred and five and one-half years after the last one of the pair until we have the first of the December pair of transits. After that it will be one hundred and twenty-one and a half years until we have the first of another pair of June transits.

The first transit of Venus that was scientifically observed was in December, 1639. It was the last of a December pair, there having been a transit eight years before, in December, 1631. One hundred and twenty-one and a half years later, in 1761, a June transit occurred, and in 1769 another one took place in June. Then there were no more for one hundred and five and one-half years, when we had a December pair in 1874 and 1882. The next ones will be in June, 2004 and 2012.

Great importance was attached to those transits that occurred in 1874 and 1882, because they were expected to be useful in determining with greater exactness the distance of the sun. Extensive preparations were made for scientific observation of them; but the results were not satisfactory, largely because the atmosphere of Venus prevented her from showing a sharp outline at the moment of entering upon and of leaving the face of the sun. The main scientific value of a transit of Venus now is in the opportunity it may offer to investigate the nature of her atmosphere. Even though that interesting question may have been practically settled before another transit takes place, it will be important to know to what degree the phenomena observed at the next transit confirm the decision.

On account of the surpassing brilliancy of Venus, the brightest of all the heavenly bodies after the sun and moon, she was to the ancients the most important of all the stars and planets. She was the supreme evening and morning star. As evening star she was known as Hesperus, or Vesper; as a morning star she was called Phosphorus, or Lucifer, and under all these names she is frequently mentioned in Greek and Latin and kindred literatures.

The symbol of Venus is ♀, a figure which is nothing more than the conventionalized form of a looking-glass, an article that is often pictured in the hands of the goddess for whom our beautiful planet was named. In her general aspect she is as placidly splendid and charming as ever a goddess could be, and it is not strange that the happy ears that could hear such strains should find her, as they did, singing a rich contralto in the music of the spheres. Jupiter and Saturn, under this mythological apportionment, sang bass, Mars took care of the tenor strains, and the high soprano was carried by our little dwarf Mercury.

XII

MARS

The planet that varies most in the beauty of its aspect is Mars. It is as much as fifty times brighter when it is nearest to us than it is at its greatest distance from us. At its brightest it is many times more brilliant than any of the first-magnitude stars; but when it leaves our neighborhood and goes far off into space in its journey around the sun, its glory is so dimmed that it becomes not brighter than an ordinary second-magnitude star, such as the pole-star, and less brilliant than the brightest stars in the Big Dipper.

These extreme changes of brightness are due not so much to any great distance that Mars goes from us in comparison with other planets as to its coming so very near to us at times. It is, after all, a small body, and no great distance, as heavenly distances go, is required to make it show so. But the eccentricity of its orbit brings it sometimes very near us, and its near approaches are at a time when we can see its entire disc, and not a mere crescent, such as we see when Venus is nearest to us. Mars does not come quite so near to us as Venus comes, but when he is in the best position to be seen he is much nearer than she is when in her best position. For we have seen that Venus is brightest before she reaches her nearest position to us, while Mars is brightest when he is at his nearest to us. When Venus is at greatest elongation she is three times farther away than Mars is at his nearest.

HOW TO IDENTIFY MARS

But with all his variations in brilliancy and beauty Mars remains ever a charming, rosy-hued planet, shining always with a steady, clear light, and when once we have come to know him is not easily mistaken for any other planet, or for any of the brilliant stars that may more or less resemble him in color. Red in varying degrees of intensity is, perhaps, the most obviously distinguishing mark of Mars; but his own characteristics are never more distinct than when his path takes him into the region of the two best-known red stars in the heavens. These are Antares, the glowing star in the constellation Scorpio, which we see in the southern sky during the summer, and ruddy Aldebaran, which shines in the head of Taurus and under the Pleiades through the bright wintry nights. On every journey around the skies

Mars passes near these two stars. They are both in the constellations of the zodiac, and are often quite near to Mars, as well as to the other planets and the moon. The stars, though of the same color as Mars, are much more jewel-like than the planet. Mars is less sparkling. When it is small, it shows a placid, rosy little disc, without much gaiety, and not in any way suggesting anything martial; but at its largest, it has a distinctly flame-like aspect, which easily suggests why it was named for the god of war.

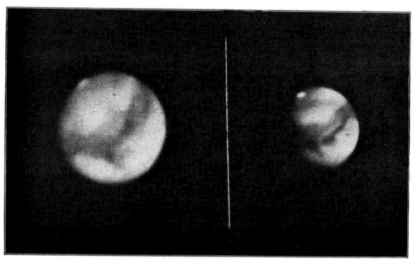

THE TWO PHASES OF MARS

We see its full face when it is opposite the sun. When half-way between opposition and conjunction it becomes gibbous, as shown in the photograph on the right. These photographs were made at the Mt. Wilson Observatory.

Mercury is the only planet that in color even suggests Mars, and for Mercury it can never be mistaken after one has once seen the two planets. Mercury, we know, is always very near the sun; but when visible at all is, even in that unfavorable situation, always as bright as a first-magnitude star. Mars is near the sun, to our view, only when it is approaching conjunction, and it is then so far from us that it always appears as a rather small star, and, while never insignificant, is, in this situation, quite inconspicuous even as compared with the rarely visible Mercury.

On seeing a planet, then, sufficiently high above the horizon to attract one's attention, one may be sure that it is Mars if it is red, and equally sure that it is not Mars if it does not show this color. Under certain atmospheric conditions the sun, moon, and all the planets sometimes appear red when they are very near the horizon; but in this situation there is always something other than color that marks them.

If its color is not a sufficient mark by which to identify Mars, a still further difference between it and the stars is its markedly rapid movement. A single night will make a sufficient change in its position to show the planet as a wanderer. On an average, it travels over about four-tenths of a degree in the heavens in one day. This equals more than half the diameter of the moon, a change of position sufficiently great to be easily detected.

WHEN AND WHERE MARS MAY BE SEEN

Unlike Mercury and Venus, which are never far from the sun, and can be seen only for a comparatively short time either early in the morning or in the evening, and are never very high up in the skies, Mars may be situated so that it can be seen at any time of the night, and also at any distance from the sun. When it is in opposition it rises just as the sun sets, and is then in view all night. At this time it is nearer, larger, and brighter than at any other time in the particular revolution it is then making, and, consequently, is in the best position to be viewed by us that it will have during that revolution.

Oppositions differ, however, in different revolutions, and some show us the planet more splendidly brilliant than it appears at others. The oppositions at which Mars shows most brilliant take place, fortunately, in the summer and early autumn—the seasons which are most agreeable for outdoor observation. He is then traveling through that region of the sky, sparse in stars, that lies between Sagittarius and Aries; and, since the ecliptic there runs rather low in the sky, he can easily be observed at any time in the night without any neck-breaking postures.

These favorable oppositions occur in the summer because the earth is in line in the latter part of August with that point in the orbit of Mars where the planet makes its nearest approach to the sun. Oppositions never occur when Mars is exactly at that point; but they do occur when he is very near it, and at such times we see him in his greatest glory. This happens once every fifteen or seventeen years. But at any summer or early-autumn opposition Mars is not very far from this nearest point to the sun, so that at any oppositions during these seasons he is very brilliant and almost as bright as when he is at his best.

The earth is in line in the winter with that part of Mars's orbit which carries him farthest from the sun, and at opposition then he is much less bright than at the summer oppositions. He is at the same time in those constellations which pass nearly overhead in the sky, and cannot be quite so comfortably seen at all times in the night as he can be in the summer. The very best and most brilliant oppositions occur in the latter part of August or in the early part of September; the least favorable ones occur in February. The others vary in brilliancy according to their distance from these favorable and unfavorable dates, all the summer ones being quite brilliant, and all the winter ones much less so. At any opposition, though, however unfavorable, the planet is much nearer to us and much brighter than when in conjunction.

It is worth one's while, even at some inconvenience, to see Mars at whatever time he is in opposition, for he is a delight to the observer, and always notable in the part of the skies through which he is then passing. There are some aspects of the planet that are so charming at a winter opposition that it is a positive loss not to have seen him at such times. He is more isolated and conspicuous in the summer; but he fits well in that gay company of winter stars that shine more brilliantly than any others, and we can easily feel something akin to family pride as we watch him moving so graciously among them.

Mars makes a complete circuit of the skies, and comes back into the same position with relation to the sun and the earth on an average every seven hundred and eighty days, which makes his synodic period longer than that of any other planet. Owing to the great eccentricity of his orbit, and his consequent unequal motion in the various parts of it, the synodic period varies as much as thirty-five or thirty-six days. One cannot say, therefore, without computation of some length, just exactly how many days will elapse between any two single oppositions.

For mere purposes of naked-eye observation the variations in the synodic period of Mars do not make any difference, for the planet is in view practically all night for many nights before and after opposition, with changes of brightness too small to be noticed by an untrained eye. For at least two months at the time of opposition it has almost the same aspect to us. At that time it is always in the east early in the evening, and shines all night. For nearly nine months afterward it is visible and conspicuous in the evening sky, appearing each evening nearer and nearer to the western horizon, until finally, in a little more than a year after opposition, it passes behind the sun and becomes a morning star. But, as it then rises before the sun and passes across the heavens in the daytime, it is invisible to us. It is pleasant, however, at such times to know that as the sun passes across the skies in its daily journey Mars is up there, within a certain distance from it, making the same journey with it, beaming down upon us with the same lively light that it shows at night, and could be as well seen at any time but for the too dazzling rays of the sun.

Mars will be in conjunction in November of this year (1912), and will not be visible in the evening during 1913 until toward the end of the year. The next opposition after the publication of this book will occur in January, 1914. From that time until the following autumn the planet may be seen in the evening. In 1915 Mars will not be visible in the evening sky until late in the year. After November it will be in the east in the evening, rising earlier each evening, until at opposition, early in 1916, it will rise at sunset and will be visible in the evening during the entire summer and autumn of that year, but will not be extraordinarily bright. In 1917 it will be again invisible in the evening. In 1918 it will be in opposition in the early spring, and will shine in the evening all the rest of that year. It will not be visible in the evening in 1919, but will be in opposition again in the latter part of April, 1920, and will shine in the evening all of that year and the early part of the next, when it will again disappear from evening view and will not emerge again until it is nearing a fine opposition that will take place just at the beginning of the summer of 1922. The planet will then be in the constellation Scorpio, not far from Antares, and this will afford an excellent opportunity to see these two ruddy bodies near together.

In 1924 there will be an exceptionally brilliant opposition, which will occur during the last week of August, and the planet will then be about as brilliant as it ever appears, and will be very favorably situated for observation in the constellation Pisces. We shall then see Mars in the flame-like phase of his beauty, and he will dominate the evening sky during the whole of that summer. At oppositions such as this one Mars is more favorably situated for observation from the earth than any other heavenly body except the moon.

The next oppositions will take place the last week in October, 1926, in December, 1928, January, 1931, early March, 1935, the middle of May, 1937; and then we will have two more splendidly brilliant oppositions in July, 1939, and early October, 1941, respectively.

During the years that Mars does not appear in the evening we need not be deprived of a sight of the planet if we will look for it in the morning sky. A few months after conjunction it may be seen as a morning star, rising shortly before the sun. It rises earlier each morning, and hence can be seen each morning for a longer time. After its hour of rising has reached midnight it then passes into the evening sky and rises earlier each evening until it reaches opposition.

The movement of Mars among the stars, as we see it, is generally toward the east, and we can see by looking that it changes its place among the constellations in that direction, going from Aries to Taurus, from Taurus to Gemini, and so on. On each side of opposition, however, the planet appears for a few weeks to be moving westward among the stars. This is the retrograde motion which an outer planet appears to have when we are overtaking and passing it, and which has been explained in the chapters on the movements of the planets.

SIZE, ATMOSPHERE, AND TEMPERATURE

In size Mars is one of the smallest members of our solar family. Its mass is a little more than one-ninth that of the earth, and its entire surface is only about one-third as great as ours. It is the merest trifle more dense than Mercury, but only about sixty-six one-hundredths as dense as the earth. Its force of gravity is about thirty-six one-hundredths as powerful as that of the earth. A man weighing two hundred pounds here would be relieved of about one hundred and twenty-four pounds of his weight if transported to Mars, weighing there only seventy-six pounds, which would greatly increase his efficiency if he were in other respects the same.

It would necessarily follow that Mars, having such small force of gravity, could not long retain a heavy atmosphere, even if it had set out with such a one. No molecule of gas moving at a greater speed than three and thirteen-hundredths miles a second could be held by Mars in its atmosphere, and so much as it may have had of the rarer gases which move with great rapidity must have escaped long ago. But it did not begin life with an atmosphere heavy in proportion to that which the larger planets have. We have seen, in the case of Mercury, that being one of the small planets entails many restrictions in development. Such planets not only lose their atmosphere more quickly than the larger ones, but it is less dense to begin with. The atmosphere of Mars is probably no denser than we have at the tops of our highest mountains, more than likely not even so dense as that. There is some water vapor, and there are a few clouds most of the time; but in the main the atmosphere is so clear and thin that we can without any doubt see the actual surface of the planet. It is not certain that the clouds we see are formed from water vapor, as clouds of the ordinary kind are. It has been suggested that they may be simply dust-clouds. But this is as yet not much more than a suggestion, and nothing convincing has been offered to substantiate the idea. Even dust-clouds would need currents of air to create and carry them; so, whether dust or vapor, the presence of clouds implies an atmosphere.

The famous white polar caps, which furnish so many news items to the journals, are also of uncertain origin, and their true nature can be determined only by a fuller knowledge of the atmosphere of Mars. They appear in the winter season on the planet and disappear in its summer, so there seems to be no doubt that they are dependent in some way on the temperature in the polar regions of Mars. If they are hoar-frost or snow, they are condensations of water vapor; and, in that case, when they disappear there must be sufficient heat to melt them. It has been contended that the sun's rays fall too obliquely on the poles of Mars to melt more than a few inches of snow, but that the caps may be light snow or frost, and thus capable of being dissolved by even such oblique rays of sunlight as they receive. Also it has been suggested that the deposit resembling snow may be carbon dioxide, which condenses into a white substance at a temperature more than a hundred degrees (-109° Fahr.) lower than is necessary to produce snow and melts at a correspondingly low temperature. What the nature of the phenomenon seen at the poles of Mars is depends largely upon what the temperature is; and the temperature in turn is dependent in some measure on the density and constitution of the atmosphere, as well as the planet's distance from the sun.

The normal temperature of an unprotected body at the distance of Mars from the sun is about thirty-two degrees blow zero (Fahrenheit); and since we know Mars has no dense atmosphere to retain the heat it acquires, it is natural to suppose the existence there of a very low temperature, and one incompatible with our ideas of life and growth. The most favorable conclusions do not place the mean temperature higher than forty-eight degrees Fahrenheit. It is certain that the planet must be subjected to great extremes of temperature within its range, since its filmy robe of atmosphere cannot protect it to any extent from the direct rays of the sun during the day, nor prevent the heat from escaping with great rapidity at night; so that, whatever heat it may gain in the daytime, it probably loses much of it during the night. Until we know more of the constitution of the atmosphere of Mars we can know nothing certainly about its temperature beyond the fact that it is much colder than ours and more subject to variations. Anything much more definite than this is speculative at present. But with all the observation that is now given to Mars, and with the always increasing facilities for the work, many uncertainties regarding the planet are likely to be made clear before long. The spectroscope will probably be the final resort for facts concerning the atmosphere.

DISTANCE AND BRILLIANCY

Mars is, on an average, about one and a half times farther from the sun than we are. Its mean distance is, in round numbers, one hundred and forty-one million miles; but, since its orbit is very eccentric—more eccentric than that of any other of the planets except Mercury—its distance from the sun varies as much as twenty-six million miles. At its nearest the planet is a little more than one hundred and twenty-eight million miles from the sun. Its greatest distance from that luminary is one hundred and fifty-four million miles. At its mean distance something more than twelve and a half minutes are required for light to travel from the sun to the planet.

The sun becomes quite a medium-sized object as viewed from Mars, and must lose some of the majesty of aspect that it has to us. Its apparent diameter is about twenty-one minutes, which would make it less than two-thirds as large as we see it. The average amount of light and heat that it furnishes to that poor, lightly clad little planet is less than half as much as we receive, though when the planet is at perihelion the sun's radiance is forty per cent. more powerful than when it is at its greatest distance from the source of these life-giving forces.

The eccentricity of the orbit of Mars is the cause also of his great variations in distance from us, and hence of his extreme changes in brilliancy. These changes are many times greater with reference to the earth than to the sun. At the planet's nearest approach to us it comes a little nearer than thirty-five millions of miles. This is when it is in opposition in August. When opposition occurs in February, it is as much as sixty-two millions of miles from us; and when it is in conjunction, and on the other side of the sun from us, it is sometimes two hundred and forty-eight million miles distant. At his nearest approach light leaps over to us from Mars in about four minutes and eighteen seconds; at his greatest distance it cannot reach us in less than twenty-two minutes. The apparent mean diameter of Mars is about nine and fifty-six hundredths seconds, but varies from three and six-tenths seconds, when the planet is farthest away, to twenty-five seconds when it is nearest to us.

While Mars does not exhibit the phases of the inner planets Venus and Mercury, by showing a disc sometimes at half-full and sometimes at crescent it is sufficiently near us to be, in certain positions, gibbous, or to show a little less than a full face. When this occurs Mars is about half-way between opposition and conjunction, and the earth and the sun are so situated that we are slightly to one side of the fully illuminated face of Mars. This phase, however, is not sufficiently marked to make any material difference in the brilliancy of the planet. It is not apparent without the aid of a telescope.

From Mars the earth shows all the phases that Venus shows to us. When Mars is flaming down upon us in his position of greatest brilliancy we present to him a thin crescent. When he sees our full face we are on the opposite side of the sun from him. It would be necessary to have a more brilliant electrical illumination than any we have yet seen to lighten the dark side of the earth and exchange signals with Mars when we are nearest to him—if, indeed, our atmosphere would permit from Mars any view at all of the surface of the earth, which is not at all certain. In spite of its phases, the earth must shine on Mars at times in a very attractive way. It is not so bright, perhaps, as Venus is to us, nor as we are to Venus; but with our moon circling about us we may well be, when in a favorable situation, a very interesting double star, the distance between earth and moon appearing on Mars about equal to one-fourth of the apparent diameter of the moon.

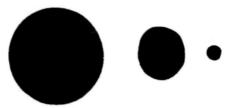

MARS: DIFFERENCE IN ITS APPARENT SIZE AT ITS NEAREST, MIDDLE, AND FARTHEST
DISTANCE FROM THE EARTH

Mars appears fifty times brighter when nearest than when farthest away.

DAY AND NIGHT, AND SEASONS

Owing to the undoubted permanent markings on the surface of Mars, astronomers have been able to determine the length of its day with much less likelihood of error than in the case of any other planet except the one on which we dwell. It rotates on its axis in twenty-four hours, thirty-seven minutes, and twenty-three seconds, which makes its day nearly forty minutes longer than ours. In our greed for all too fleeting time we may feel a little envy of these extra minutes, which would mean so much to us if added to our day. But they do not seem so important when we consider that while Mars is having six hundred and seventy of these days we are having six hundred and eighty-seven of ours, which, after all, seems to give us eighteen days more of time. Our attitude toward the situation depends upon the point of view.

The axis of Mars is inclined to its orbit about twenty-four degrees and fifty minutes. This is but little more than the inclination of the earth's axis, which is twenty-three degrees and twenty-seven minutes. Mars, therefore, has seasons very much like ours. They are, however, slightly more marked than ours, because of the somewhat greater inclination of the axis of the planet; and they are nearly double the length of ours, because it takes Mars nearly two of our years to make its journey around the sun. Its seasons, then, are nearly six months long, while ours are but three. It has frigid, temperate, and torrid zones, practically the same as the earth has. Its greatest inequalities of season are caused by the eccentricity of its orbit. It is, like the earth, farthest away from the sun when it is summer in the northern hemisphere; and in this situation it travels so much more slowly than when it is near the sun that summer in its northern hemisphere is seventy-five days longer than the same season in the southern hemisphere. The northern summer and the southern winter are each three hundred and eighty days long, while the reverse seasons in each hemisphere are only three hundred and six days long. The northern summer is not only longer but also cooler than the southern, and the northern winter is shorter and warmer than the southern. Which hemisphere has the more favorable climate depends upon what is needed on Mars to maintain life. It may be that in this regard the shorter, hotter, southern summer is the best season the planet affords.

SURFACE ASPECTS OF MARS

Seen through a telescope, Mars is not so red as it appears to the naked eye. One of the best observers of it has compared it to an opal, and it surely has some of the qualities of an opal in the diversity of aspect that it shows to different observers from different points of view. No other planet has been so subjected to controversy over what appears on its surface. This is partly due to its being the only planet whose surface is without doubt open to our view and in a situation where it can be minutely studied, and partly to the fact that the controversy involves questions concerning life and intelligence, which are always of intense human interest. Matters of this vital sort are never accepted without dispute. That is one way of getting at the truth. In the intensity of the discussion the question of the existence of the phenomena and that of the meaning ascribed to them are sometimes unnecessarily made to depend upon each other. In the case of Mars it may well be that there is less difference of opinion as to what is really seen on its surface than as to the meaning of the phenomena.

There are recorded observations made of Mars as early as 272 B.C., more than two thousand years ago, and it has been nearly two hundred and fifty years since the snow-caps were first seen. Through the telescope not only the snow-caps are plainly visible at the proper seasons, but there are also visible dark patches over the surface, showing a variety of color, and in certain parts changing somewhat as the seasons change. It is one of these patches, the outline of which suggests a somewhat twisted eye, that is known as the "eye of Mars." The main surface of the planet is reddish yellow in color; the patches on it are variously described as gray, grayish green, or blue, colors which in combination could easily take on a tone of any of them according to the eye of the observer, and this portion of the planet's surface does, in fact, show first one and then the other of them predominating.

When the planet's differences of color were first observed, the reddish-yellow portion was supposed to be land, and the areas of varying bluish-green and gray were thought to be the waters of the ever-changing seas. A little after the middle of the last century some keen eyes saw a few streaks or markings of some sort across the land areas, and in 1877 a close study of the planet by an eminent Italian astronomer, Schiaparelli, brought to his view many greenish streaks, all directed toward the so-called seas, and sometimes seeming to intersect there. In publishing this discovery Schiaparelli called these streaks *canalli*, which is properly translated "channels," but appeared in English as "canals." Since "canal" with us means artificially constructed waterways, the discovery became at once one of universal interest; for artificial waterways mean human beings to construct them, and it was an intensely interesting thing to know that Mars was probably inhabited with beings at least somewhat after our own kind. It was a new world. The little planet became a topic of absorbing interest to all of us. And thus began the controversy over the habitability of Mars, and the meaning of its surface features, in which astronomers, seeking only for the truth, have taken a much more dignified part than they have sometimes been more or less sensationally represented as doing. The discoverer of the so-called canals himself believed them to be natural waterways cutting through the land after the manner of our straits and channels, and had very little to say in explanation of them. But his work gave a new impetus to the study of this little brother world of ours.

In our own country the observatory at Flagstaff is the one the best known among those doing research work on Mars; but it is not the only one. The observatory there is finely situated in the thin, clear atmosphere of Arizona, the mechanical facilities for such work are good, and there seems no doubt that there are there some observers who have eyes that were made for seeing. All that the sharp vision of Schiaparelli saw has been seen there, and much more. Several hundred canals have been discovered, and at certain seasons many of them have appeared to become double. Their courses have been followed, and their appearances and disappearances have been watched. Somewhere near six hundred of them have been mapped. According to these maps, the canals seem to be laid out with a geometrical precision such as nature is not likely to follow; they run across some regions that were formerly supposed to be water, and they have points of convergence every here and there, forming at such points large dark areas.

Naturally, when a person has discovered any new and curious phenomenon in nature he seeks to determine the exact meaning of it. It would have very little interest for him if he did not, and it would be a dry lot of facts that did not arouse a desire to do this. The interpretation put upon what has been seen at the observatory at Flagstaff is, in brief, about as follows:

The surface of Mars has no oceans or mountains. The reddish areas, which form the larger part of the surface, are deserts. The blue-green streaks are ribbons of vegetation along each side of artificially constructed waterways, which are of immense length and cross and recross each other until they somewhat resemble a network of lines over the desert surface of the planet, and are used for irrigating this arid region. The points where the canals converge and form the large dark spots are oases made by the water carried by the canals. The water is supplied by the melting of the caps of snow at the poles during the Martian summer, the expanding of the lines of vegetation seeming to occur at periods corresponding to the time required for the water of the melting snow to reach the oases. The presence of this vast system of artificial waterways covering a large part of the surface of Mars makes it seem probable that "Mars is inhabited by beings of some sort or other," that these beings are not men such as we know anything about, but that "there may be a local intelligence equal to or superior to ours."

These conclusions concerning what is seen on Mars are not held by any one to be completely proved, but are thought by their author to follow reasonably from the phenomena as observed. By persons of a different temperament they are regarded as too complete an explanation, particularly as the data upon which they are founded are not undisputed. Some of the best astronomers have not been able even to see the multitude of fine lines, much less to give any explanation of them. Others do not regard it as certain that they are so geometric in their outlines as to suggest anything more than cracks or clefts in the surface of Mars, such as might be made by nature, and consider that, instead of indicating life, human or other, they may be the marks of age, such as similar lines or cracks which have been observed on Mercury seem to be.

Also, it is not at all certain that there is sufficient water vapor in the slight atmosphere of Mars to furnish the snow necessary for this great irrigating system, nor the heat to melt it at the proper season. The natural temperature of Mars would be, as we have seen, very low, and unless it is modified in some way not yet indicated everything points to a frigidity too intense to permit the continuance of life and growth of any sort known to us.

These things must all be reckoned with before anything certain can be known of the surface of Mars. The difficulty of pronouncing upon the minute details is impressively indicated by Professor Moulton, who says that, even under the finest conditions and with the best telescopes, it is like viewing "a perfectly accurate relief map of the whole United States made on such a scale that it would be only three inches in diameter and held at a distance of three feet from the eye." Under such a near limit of vision, we can well see that differences of opinion might arise.

The mere fact that some astronomers have not seen the lines on Mars does not mean that they deny their existence. Some eyes have greater defining power than others, as well as some telescopes, as every one knows. But while all the lines and patches of color that are claimed to have been seen on Mars doubtless have been seen by some persons, yet it is not necessary to accept the interpretation of them given by lively-minded observers when it is not convincing. There may be vegetation on Mars, and even intelligent beings. We do not know; and thus far there is not much to support, even by inference, the view that there are. If we want the truth, we are brought no nearer to it by giving full credence to a speculative theory simply because it is interesting and pleasant; and thus far all theories advanced as to the nature of the surface markings on Mars are speculations, though there is no doubt that the marks are there. It is pleasing, however, to contemplate the idea of there being on Mars, or on any other planet, an active intelligence of any sort resembling what we have here on earth, and it is not strange that such a wide-spread popular interest should attach to Mars, in view of what has been suggested by the markings on its surface.

THE SATELLITES OF MARS

Mars has a little family of two moons. Tiny little bodies they are, the smallest in the solar family except, perhaps, an occasional asteroid. Neither one of them is more than ten miles in diameter, and the two together are smaller than any other known satellite. They can only be seen when Mars is in opposition, and then only with a fairly large telescope. They were discovered in 1877, and named Phobos and Deimos, the names of the two attendants of the god of war. Phobos is the brighter and the nearer to the planet. It is less than four thousand miles from the surface of Mars; and on account of its being so near and the shape of Mars being a spheroid, like that of the earth, the little satellite can never be seen from Mars beyond sixty-nine degrees of latitude on each side of the equator. Within these limits it shows great activity. It makes a complete circuit around Mars in seven and a half hours; and this swift revolution, combined with the motion of Mars on its axis, makes Phobos seem to rise in the west and set in the east, pass over the heavens in less than twelve hours, and go through all its phases, from "new" to "full," one and a half times every night. Its light is rather insignificant, being about sixty times less than we receive from our satellite; but, on the whole, it must be a rather gay and pleasant little moon.

Deimos is not any larger than Phobos, and not as bright; but it is slightly less difficult for us to see, because it is between two and three times farther away from Mars than Phobos is, and thus not so much lost in the light of the planet. It circles around Mars in a little more than thirty hours, and this, being only six hours more than Mars consumes in turning around on its axis, results in requiring more than two days for the satellite to pass from rising to setting. Between rising and setting it goes through its phases four times. It can be seen from all parts of Mars, but gives very little light to the planet—more than a thousand times less than our moon gives us.

The symbol of Mars is ♂, a conventionalized figure representing a shield and a spear—implements of war appropriate for the use of the deity especially connected with warfare.

XIII

JUPITER

One never feels so impressed with the power of the sun as when one contemplates it in relation to Jupiter. Great Jupiter, he may well be called, nearly five hundred million miles out in space, almost a sun himself, the center of a system containing bodies larger than the sun's nearest planet, Mercury; and yet just Jupiter, one of the planets, held firmly in leash like the others by the sun's overwhelming force of gravity, forever compelled to revolve about that parent body with the rest of its offspring, to stay at home within the bounds of the sun's domain, to keep within certain limits in his own orbit, forced to hasten on when he comes nearest the power that controls him, and unable to keep up the same rate of speed when he is farther away. One may well wonder at the immensity beyond comprehension of the stars, among which our sun is but a very small one, when one considers how even this small one can thus swing huge Jupiter about. For Jupiter is, after the sun itself, the mammoth member of our system. In volume he is larger than all the other planets put together, and in mass he is more than double as large as the combined mass of all the others. He is about equal to the sun in density, and about one-fourth as dense as the earth.

There is less difference in size between Jupiter and the sun than there is between Jupiter and the earth. His diameter is eleven times greater than that of the earth. The sun's diameter is only ten times greater than Jupiter's. His surface is one hundred and sixteen times that of the earth; the sun's own surface is only a hundred times larger than his. Jupiter weighs more than three hundred times as much as the earth; the sun weighs only six times more than Jupiter. At the equator his diameter is about ninety thousand miles; but, as the planet is much flattened at the poles, the diameter from pole to pole is only a little more than eighty-four thousand miles. This flattening is due to the very rapid spinning of the planet on its axis, a motion that will always cause a plastic body to bulge at the equator, and thus flatten at the poles.

JUPITER, THE MAMMOTH MEMBER OF THE SOLAR FAMILY—LARGER THAN ALL THE
OTHER PLANETS PUT TOGETHER

This photograph shows the flattening at the poles and also the belts encircling the planet. It was
photographed at the Yerkes Observatory.

The force of gravity on Jupiter is about two and one-half times greater than on
the earth. A fairy-like figure weighing here only a hundred pounds would be
held to the surface of Jupiter with a force equal to two hundred and sixty
pounds. This tremendous power makes Jupiter the greatest disturbing body
among all the planets. He gives Saturn a mighty pull when the two planets
come near each other; he draws some of the little asteroids five or six degrees
out of their course when it carries them into the field of his influence; and
there are as many as thirty comets that have become permanent members of
the solar system, because through his great power of attraction he has made
them captive.

Jupiter is so much farther from the sun than we are that his orbit is about five times larger than that of the earth. In consequence also of his greater distance from the sun, he moves much more slowly than the earth. His average velocity is about eight miles a second. It requires more than four thousand days, or nearly twelve of our years, for him to make one revolution around the sun, and he thus consumes more than ten thousand of his own days. He travels through about one sign of the zodiac each year, and is thus not very difficult to keep trace of, since the signs and the constellations of the zodiac so nearly coincide. His synodic period, or the period from one opposition to another, is a fraction less than three hundred and ninety-nine days, or about one year and a little more than a month. His daily motion in the skies is almost too small for us to detect it without observation for more than a day. It is in one day about equal to one-sixth of the apparent diameter of the moon; but in a month he has moved a distance about half as great as that between the two pointers in the Big Dipper, as can be easily seen by comparison with the stars near him.

JUPITER'S PLACE IN THE SKY

Jupiter is now (1912) in the constellation Scorpio, and he will be in this region, and thus a summer star, for several years to come. In 1913 he will be in opposition early in July, and will then be in Sagittarius, not far from the little "milk dipper," and will be a gloriously beautiful object during all the summer. He will be in opposition about August 10, 1914, in Capricornus, and will again be the most brilliant object in the summer sky. In 1915 he will be in opposition a little after the middle of September, and will then be situated on or near the eastern edge of Aquarius, where he will be a very distinguished star during all the charming evenings of late summer and the autumn. He always seems particularly splendid when in this season of the year he reaches opposition. The insistent brilliancy of his disc brings him then into view before the sun is fairly down; and he hangs, placid and alone, in the southeastern sky during the autumn twilight, and later in the evening shows to advantage his dominating beauty, with Antares on the west of him and Fomalhaut below him, no less charming in their own way, but far less brilliant than this splendid planet.

In 1916, when opposition will occur not far from Hallowe'en, Jupiter will be about on the eastern border of the constellation Pisces, and, rising then just as the sun sets, will enliven the evening view for the rest of that year. He will appear at his very best at this time, for he will be at about his nearest to the sun; and all that this situation can do for him in the way of enhancing his brilliancy may then be seen.

In 1917 he will be in opposition to the sun about the first of December, in Taurus; and for the next few years he will be a winter star, moving majestically along his path in the zodiac, never more than one and a half degrees from the ecliptic, and passing in turn the Pleiades, Aldebaran, Castor and Pollux, and the little Bee-hive in Cancer. There will be no opposition in 1918; but one will occur early in January, 1919, when Jupiter is in the eastern half of Gemini; and toward the middle of February, 1920, another will take place, when the planet is in Cancer, with Castor and Pollux, the sparkling twin stars in Gemini, to the west of him.

During part of 1920 and all of the next three years Jupiter will be journeying across Leo, Virgo, Libra, and Scorpio. He will be opposite the sun in 1921, a little after the middle of March; in 1922, in the latter half of April; and in 1923, toward the very last of May. He will pass near Regulus, the sparkling star in the handle of the Sickle, in the summer of 1920; near Spica in 1921; and he will not be far from Antares in 1923.

In 1924 Jupiter's cycle of twelve years will be completed, and he will be in opposition again early in July, and situated near the western edge of Sagittarius, not far from where he was in 1912.

These cycles do not repeat themselves exactly; but the planet lacks only four days of having been in opposition eleven times during twelve of our years, so that it is not difficult to keep track of him through a long series of years. For exact dates, such as one needs in a very close study of the planet, an almanac must be consulted; but this is not necessary for mere recognition, which is all that is needed to enjoy the acquaintance of great Jupiter.

Every year Jupiter is an evening star for more than six months. For two months before opposition he rises somewhat after sundown; at opposition he appears exactly at the setting of the sun; and thereafter he is found in the evening sky, appearing farther toward the west each evening, until, when nearing conjunction, he is lost to our view for a time. He is a morning star for an equal length of time, and for about three months can be seen between midnight and six in the morning; but much of the rest of the time he is obscured by the daylight.

Jupiter retrogrades in his motion for about two months before and after each opposition; but, since he changes his place to the extent of only two and a half degrees a month, the whole apparently backward movement amounts only to ten degrees a year. Still, it is very interesting to watch him swing back and forth over this ten degrees before he starts out on each yearly journey.

DISTANCE, LIGHT, AND HEAT

Jupiter is nearly five times farther from the sun than we are. His mean distance from that orb is four hundred and eighty-three millions of miles. His orbit is not so eccentric as that of Mercury or of Mars, but the eccentricity is sufficient to make his distance vary by as much as forty-two millions of miles. His distance is five hundred and four millions of miles when he is farthest from the sun, and four hundred and sixty-two millions when he is nearest to it. On account of his orbit being outside of ours, we are at times nearer to him and at others farther from him than the sun ever is. At his best situation when in opposition, we are three hundred and sixty-nine million miles from him. This is more than ten times farther than we are from Mars at that planet's most favorable oppositions, and yet Jupiter is much brighter at such times than Mars ever appears to be. At the times of conjunction he is five hundred and ninety-six millions of miles from us, but is still always brighter than a first-magnitude star like Capella or Vega.

Although the distance of Jupiter from us varies thus two hundred and twenty-seven million miles, there is never in him the marked difference in brilliancy that we see in Mars. He is at all times so far away that the variation in distance does not count for as much, though we can see the effect of it plainly enough, even with the naked eye. Light, with all its marvelous speed, consumes more than fifty-three minutes in its journey from Jupiter to the earth when we are most widely separated from him. When we are nearest to him light comes to us from the planet in twenty minutes less time. At his average distance from the sun it requires about forty-three minutes for light to pass from the sun to Jupiter.

Notwithstanding the sun's great power over Jupiter in shaping his course, it does not give him much in return for his subserviency. So far as light and brilliancy are concerned, it is to Jupiter a very small sun indeed. To an observer on Jupiter the sun would not appear to be more than one-fifth as large as it seems to us. The light it furnishes to Jupiter is twenty-five times less than we receive; and if the planet depended entirely upon the sun for heat, his temperature would be more than two hundred degrees below zero, Fahrenheit. There is every reason to believe that the little heat the sun gives to this mighty planet does not count for much one way or the other at the planet's present stage of development. Jupiter does not need the nourishing that the smaller terrestrial planets must have, or die. He is probably almost a sun himself. We are not at all certain that the planet is even so far cooled as to have a solid surface. If it has, there is reason to think that the surface is at least red hot, and gives to the planet a temperature higher than anything we have any comprehension of. Jupiter's atmosphere, too, is extremely thick and dense, so that the planet is probably so protected that it gets very little heat from the sun and loses very little of its own.

It is certain, however, that this great planet is not so much of a sun as to shine by its own light. The light we receive, though it is very brilliant, is reflected sunlight. This is shown by the fact that the planet does not furnish light for its own satellites. When they pass into its shadow the sunlight is shut off from them; and if they receive any light from Jupiter, it is too dusky to be perceptible to us. That the planet may have a red glow, though, is also suggested by the action of the satellites. When they pass between us and Jupiter they sometimes cast less of a shadow on his surface than would be expected, thus indicating that the surface is not altogether dark, though it may only dully glow rather than shine.

DAY AND NIGHT, SEASONS, AND ATMOSPHERE

Jupiter accomplishes one rotation in a little less than ten hours; but, curiously enough, all parts of the planet do not rotate in the same length of time. A day at the equator is nine hours and fifty minutes in length. In some of the higher latitudes it is nine hours and fifty-five minutes, and this notwithstanding the equator is so much larger in circumference than any other part and any one point on it has farther to go in a revolution. As many as eight different rates of rotation have been observed; and even in the same zones some parts seem to lag behind others, taking a little more time to complete the rotation than other parts surrounding them. This is another indication that Jupiter is not a solid body. The surface features are none of them permanent, though some of them remain practically the same for years. It is through this occasional stability of them that it has been possible to mark the planet's time of rotation.

In the matter of seasons Jupiter has very little variety. The axis of the planet is inclined but little more than three degrees to its orbit, so that whatever amount of heat the sun's radiance affords must be very nearly uniform during the entire Jovian year. Its distance, too, is at all times so great that there would be no appreciable change in temperature between its perihelion and aphelion positions.

There is every indication that Jupiter has an extraordinarily dense and deep atmosphere. It has been sometimes estimated to be as much as a thousand miles in depth, and the spectroscope shows it to be heavily laden with vapor. But beyond these very general facts not much is definitely known about it. It is certain, though, that it is very different from our atmosphere. The spectroscope shows in it elements, or compounds of elements, which are not familiar to us. The enormous gravitative power of Jupiter would enable him to hold gases rarer than the earth, or the smaller planets like the earth, ever acquired. A molecule of gas would have to move more rapidly than thirty-seven miles a second to escape from Jupiter. The earth, as we have seen, cannot hold any gases moving faster than seven miles a second. So there are many gases which may forever remain in Jupiter's atmosphere and yet have never had a place in ours.

SURFACE FEATURES

Seen through a telescope, Jupiter shows the loveliest variety of colors, with the reddish ones always most conspicuous. The slightly pink-tinted steady light that we get from the planet with the naked eye in no way suggests the turbulent, flame-like aspect that a telescopic view opens to us. The telescope also reveals very clearly that flattening at the poles which has already been spoken of.

With so dense an atmosphere as Jupiter most likely has, it is sometimes doubtful whether his surface can be seen by us at all. But it is certain that we see something apparently much more dense and stable than an atmosphere is supposed to be; and hence it is thought that, in spite of its thickness, the atmosphere may be only partially opaque, and that it may be in some places even more or less transparent.

It does not seem probable that the markings on Jupiter are wholly atmospheric. Some of them indicate that the substance we see has considerably more consistency than a mere gas. The whole surface of the planet is covered with belts and spots of various colors and varying shapes. The belted appearance is particularly marked. It has been noticed for more than two hundred years, and can be seen with a comparatively small telescope. Sometimes as many as twenty or thirty belts have been seen at one time. All of them are parallel with the equator.

Two broad red belts on each side of the equator, called the tropical belts, are very distinct, and sometimes retain the same shape and color for months at a time, though sometimes they change rapidly in both color and outline. Between them is the equatorial belt, which is also a semi-permanent feature, remaining often for a considerable period unchanged. These belts, and the spots that sometimes appear on and near them, have been closely watched, because about the equator, and especially just south of it, is the region of greatest activity on Jupiter's surface.

One feature that more nearly suggests solidity and permanency than anything else on Jupiter is the famous great red spot which lies in the southern hemisphere just below the southern tropical belt. It appeared about thirty-five years ago, in July, 1878, as a pale pink spot, grew brighter for two or three years, and then faded, until, at the end of two or three more years, it was almost invisible. In another year it came again, and increased in brightness for five or six years. Then it grew a little fainter, and has since remained a rather faint red spot, but plainly visible.

In shape the great red spot is an immense oval as much as thirty thousand miles from east to west and seven thousand miles from north to south, which gives it a surface four or five times as large as the land area on the entire earth, and larger even than the whole surface of the earth including the oceans. Although retaining its own shape, it seems to drift about among its surroundings, showing that it is not attached to any solid surface; and yet it has a suggestion of solidity in itself, which was shown when it and another smaller spot were seen to be drifting toward each other, and then finally to meet. Instead of colliding or going over or under, they calmly drifted to one side and went around each other.

Appearances such as this have suggested the idea that the great spot might be a continent in process of formation. Such an idea is at best a speculation; but it would be interesting if it should prove that we are witnessing on Jupiter the process through which our own earth must at one time have passed when its crust began to solidify in patches, as one of the steps in the long period of evolution which has prepared it for our uses. It is not at all certain that Jupiter will ever be just like the earth. The differences between its atmosphere and ours may have some influence in its development that we have little knowledge of at present, and there are some other fundamental differences between the two planets which may in some way effect a difference in development. But in a general way we know that the planet will in time become more condensed than it now is and will finally solidify. Whether the processes will be carried on in just the same way in which they have been here on the earth is not so certain.

JUPITER'S SYSTEM OF SATELLITES

Jupiter is the center of a superb system of satellites, eight in number. Four of them were first seen in 1610, and have the honor to be the first heavenly bodies discovered by means of the telescope. The fifth one was not discovered until 1892. The sixth was first seen in 1904, and the seventh in 1905. After three years an eighth was discovered (in 1908).

When the first four satellites were discovered they were named respectively, in the order of their distances from Jupiter, Io, Europa, Ganymede, and Callisto. Ganymede is not only the largest of the four, but is also the largest satellite in the solar system. It is larger than Mercury, and not much smaller than Mars. Callisto is next to Ganymede in size, and is about the size of Mercury. Io is about the size of our moon, and Europa is not much smaller. Under very favorable conditions Ganymede and Callisto can be seen by the naked eye; but a good many persons think they see the moons of Jupiter when they see only some small stars in that region. They are invisible to most people, but probably could be seen oftener if it were not for the glaring light of the planet, which more or less obscures anything so near it.

After the discovery of Jupiter's fifth satellite, astronomers seem to have become possessed with that dull spirit of orderliness such as is sometimes exhibited by city councils in substituting numbers for historic and beautiful names in designating streets. No more of Jupiter's satellites were given names such as might be appropriate for members of this Jovian family; but all were given numbers—the first four in order of their distance from Jupiter, the others in order of their discovery. Io, Europa, Ganymede, and Callisto are now designated, respectively, I, II, III, and IV, while V, VI, VII, and VIII have never had any designation other than these numbers.

The fifth satellite, discovered in 1892, is the nearest to Jupiter, and the smallest of all his satellites. Its diameter is probably not more than one hundred and twenty miles, but its exact size can be estimated only by the amount of light it reflects. It is too small to show a measurable disc, and cannot even be seen when it makes a transit across the planet. It would seem then a mere speck, if we could see it at all. It makes one revolution about Jupiter in less than twelve hours (eleven hours and fifty-seven minutes), and is only a little more than twenty-two thousand miles from the surface of the planet at the equator. It appears to us as a star of about the thirteenth magnitude, and cannot be seen except with a large telescope. Owing to the great curvature of the planet, and to the satellite's being so near him, it cannot be seen from the surface of Jupiter beyond sixty-five degrees of latitude. It moves faster than any other satellite in the solar system, going at the rate of sixteen and a half miles a second. It does not make a revolution in as short a time as Phobos, the little satellite of Mars, does, but it has a much longer distance to travel and goes at a faster rate. The fact that Jupiter rotates in ten hours and the satellite makes a revolution around him in twelve hours results in the satellite's taking five of Jupiter's days to cross from the eastern horizon to the western. It would go through all its phases four times during that period if it were not that, being so near the planet, his huge form cuts off the sunlight from the little satellite for nearly one-fifth of the time, and it is never seen "full."

This satellite is very difficult for us to see on account of its diminutive size and its nearness to the shining disc of Jupiter; yet it was discovered by means of the telescope, and not by photography, as so many small bodies are discovered nowadays, and by a man who thus far has not been able to see the fine line markings on Mars, which some other astronomers think they can see —a fact that is very interesting as showing the difference between observers even of great keenness of vision. From this satellite Jupiter would seem an enormous body, nearly eighty-five times larger than our sun appears to us, and, no doubt, a splendid object. But the little satellite pays rather dearly for the view by suffering numerous and long-continued eclipses.

The sixth and seventh satellites are also very minute bodies, measuring probably less than one hundred miles in diameter. They circle about Jupiter at a distance nearly thirty times more remote than our moon is from us. They are about seven million miles from the planet, and probably not more than barely visible from it. It takes them two hundred and sixty-five days to make one revolution, which is more than five hundred times as long as the period of Jupiter's nearest satellite. These two satellites are so nearly of one size and revolve so nearly in the same time and at the same distance from Jupiter that they are thought to have had a common origin. Just what their relation is has not yet been determined.

The eighth satellite, discovered in January, 1908, is certainly no larger, and is perhaps still more tiny, than the sixth and the seventh, though it is a little brighter than either one of them. It is about three times farther away from Jupiter than the seventh satellite, and with eyes such as ours would not be visible from Jupiter. It shows to us as about a seventeenth-magnitude star, which is almost at the limit of our vision with even the largest telescope. It seems to revolve about Jupiter in a direction exactly opposite to that of the other satellites—a retrograde motion that appears in the solar system in only two or three other cases and has not yet been entirely accounted for.

Jupiter's satellites have played an important part in astronomical discoveries and investigations. It was through observation of their transits that it was discovered that light occupied time in passing through space. When Jupiter was near us in his orbit, the eclipses occurred too soon for their calculated time; when he was farther away, they occurred too late. It was found that these irregularities were due to the fact that light is not transmitted through space instantaneously, and further investigation showed that it travels at the rate of 186,400 miles a second. The eclipses of Jupiter's moons are carefully computed and recorded in the *Nautical Almanac*, and it is through observations of them that chronometers are corrected at sea.

Ganymede and Callisto have been found to keep always the same face toward the planet, as our moon keeps always the same face toward us; and it is thought that all of Jupiter's satellites probably do this.

The symbol of Jupiter is ♃, a hieroglyph for the eagle, which was the bird of Jove.

XIV

SATURN

Among the four planets that we commonly see, the easiest, perhaps, to keep track of is Saturn. Its peculiar aspect is very distinctly marked. It appears as a large, pale, yellow star shining with a soft, misty light that sometimes barely escapes being dull. It is always as bright as a first-magnitude star, but not always as bright as Sirius, and never as brilliant as Mars, Jupiter, or Venus when they are at their brightest. The general effect of it is as a large rather than a brilliant star.

The only time it loses these very marked characteristics is when it is drawing in toward the sun, and thus nearing conjunction. At such times we see it each evening lower in the rosy glow of the setting sun, and more and more obscured and changed in color by the surrounding atmosphere. Then it sometimes seems as red as Mercury, and sometimes even twinkles a little in a sort of farewell gaiety as it backs away from us into the rays of the dazzling sun and finally disappears for a time from the evening sky. Proximity to the sun and entanglement in the atmosphere of the horizon has this effect more or less on all the planets, as we know, but it always seems unexpected in Saturn, because it is so out of keeping with his ordinarily large, pale, placid face, which suggests softness and gentleness rather than vivacity.

But there is no mistaking the planet even under this aspect if we but stop to think where he is. And it is through knowing where he is that it is so easy to keep track of Saturn. For nearly two years and a half, on an average, he remains in the same constellation, passing slowly over about one degree a month, or a little more than twelve degrees in a year, occupying almost thirty years in making one circuit through the constellations of the zodiac. One has, therefore, ample time to get well acquainted with him before he has wandered far from the position in which one first found him.

For nearly six months each year Saturn shines as an evening star, and, returning each year as he does with such slight changes of position, he comes to have something of the stability of a fixed star. Having seen him one year, we can count on his returning the next only about thirteen days behind time, and but little farther from his original position than twice the distance between the pointers in the Big Dipper.

The one degree a month which he travels along the ecliptic is toward the east, except for a little more than two months before opposition, and the same length of time afterward, when he has the slight apparent retrograde motion due to our overtaking and passing him, which has been explained. With Saturn this motion is so slight—only four degrees—that it does not put him much out of position, and it is, in fact, not much noticed except by close observers. He has all the time been going steadily on toward the east (for the retrograde motion is only an apparent motion), and the annual change of twelve degrees in position is always in this direction.

My first acquaintance with Saturn was when he was traveling through Pisces and Aries, where there are no first-magnitude stars to mark the path of the wandering bodies in the heavens. It was then that I was most impressed with the fixity and reliability of his return. Every autumn then for five years we watched Antares passing toward the west, followed by the little "milk dipper" in Sagittarius; and then Fomalhaut, crossing the sky in the same direction, though below the constellations of the zodiac; and then turned our eyes toward the east, knowing that the next bright body to come peeping over the tops of the trees would be Saturn. And when the first frosts began to strip the leaves from the trees we found the compensation that nature always gives when she destroys one beauty: we could see earlier in the evening, through the bare branches, that lovely yellowish disc, with its suggestion of aloofness and grandeur that is peculiar to it. For the face of Saturn, while never what we would call cold, has little in it of that bright, warm, friendly aspect which is at times so characteristic of Venus, Mars, and Jupiter.

AROUND ONE CIRCUIT OF THE SKIES WITH SATURN

Saturn is now (the autumn of 1912) in the first part of his path through Taurus, and he will be in that constellation during all of 1913 and the greater part of 1914.

From 1912 to 1920 he will be a beautiful object in the winter sky, threading his way slowly through that splendid galaxy of stars that blazes across the glittering sky peculiar to the cold winter nights. He will pass between the Pleiades and Aldebaran, and will be in opposition in that region on November 23, 1912. Farther east in the constellation he will be in opposition in the first week of December, 1913. Almost on the border line between Taurus and Gemini he will be in opposition during the third week in December, 1914; and, as this is very near the perihelion point in Saturn's orbit, the planet will then be at his brightest.

In 1915 he will not be in opposition at all; but sometime within the first two or three days of 1916 he will reach that position, and will then be well on in his journey across Gemini. For these four years—from 1912 to 1916—he will be visible during the entire night, at the times of his opposition, and in his best condition. The rings that surround him will then be placed so that we will get a broad expanse of light from them, as well as from the planet itself, which greatly increases its brightness.

Saturn will then continue to move across Gemini, passing in the early part of 1917 under Castor and Pollux, and very near to Neptune—a meeting which, unfortunately, cannot be seen with the naked eye. During this year (1917) he will begin his journey through the smallest of all the constellations of the zodiac, Cancer, passing near the lovely cluster of stars we call the Bee-hive, and will reach Leo early in 1919, where he will remain until about the end of 1921. While in this region he will be visible during the winter and all of the spring and the early summer. All three of these constellations—Gemini, Cancer, and Leo—while seen in the winter, are particularly lovely in the spring. Gemini, in the beautiful evenings of May, hangs with its two splendid stars in the northwest above the setting sun; and with the soft face of Saturn near them, these stars will be more than ever charming in the two seasons that the planet remains with them.

In 1917 Saturn will be in opposition in the region of Gemini, about the middle of January. In 1918 opposition will occur about the last of January, and Saturn will then be in Cancer. The next year he will be in opposition sometime during the second week in February, and will then be situated between the Bee-hive, in Cancer, and the brilliant first-magnitude star Regulus, in Leo. The next two oppositions will be in Leo, about thirteen days later each year. Saturn will then pass during the first half of 1922 into Virgo, which is the largest of all the constellations, and he will remain there until three oppositions have taken place, about thirteen days later each year.

About a year after passing Spica, the white, sparkling, first-magnitude star in Virgo, Saturn will enter Libra, crossing that constellation near the lower part of the square in it. From there he will go through Scorpio and Sagittarius, passing above Antares and the "milk dipper," and in about 1932 will have reached that comparatively starless region which includes a part of Sagittarius and all of Capricornus, Aquarius, Pisces, and Aries. For the next nine and a half years he will give distinction to this part of the heavens, and thus complete his circuit of twenty-nine and a half years, and, with never resting, never changing movement, will start on a new round, with a new generation of eyes following his fair face along the great circle of the ecliptic.

Saturn is brightest when he is in Taurus, not far from Gemini, as he will be in 1914, and again when he is in Scorpio, as he will be between fourteen and fifteen years later. The recurring times at which we can get an evening view of him at his greatest brightness thus alternate between midwinter and midsummer. He is least bright when he is in the last half of Leo and when he is in that part of Aquarius above Fomalhaut. Between these positions he gradually waxes and wanes in brightness, changes that are largely due to the position of his rings.

DISTANCE AND SIZE

Saturn is almost twice as far from the sun as Jupiter, and between nine and ten times farther than we are. His mean distance from the sun is eight hundred and eighty-seven million miles; but his distance varies nearly one hundred million miles between perihelion and aphelion. His orbit is only a trifle more eccentric than that of Jupiter, but the variation in miles is so much greater because the orbit is so much larger.

His average distance from the earth at opposition is seven hundred and ninety-four million miles, but at the most favorable opposition it may be fifty million miles nearer than that. At conjunction his average distance is nine hundred and eighty million miles; but his greatest possible distance at such times may be as much as one billion miles. When he is in this situation it takes light a little more than an hour and a half to pass from him to us. At his nearest we receive light from him in about an hour and six minutes. At his average distance from the sun, light requires about an hour and twenty minutes to go from one to the other.

While Saturn is next to Jupiter in size among the planets, he is not as large as Jupiter by two-thirds, but his mass is almost three times greater than that of all the other planets put together except Jupiter. It is ninety-five times greater than that of the earth. In diameter Saturn is 72,772 miles; but it is more flattened at the poles than any other planet, and in consequence there is a difference of nearly seven thousand miles between its polar and its equatorial diameters.

The density of Saturn is less than that of any other planet, and it is ten times less than that of the earth. No other planet is less dense than water; but Saturn would float in water, and is not more dense than cork. On account of its mass its gravity is greater than that of the earth by about one-tenth. This is not enough to make a very interesting difference in the weight of objects on Saturn and on the earth. The average person weighing one hundred and fifty pounds here would weigh only one hundred and sixty-five pounds on Saturn. The numerous penny-in-the-slot weighing-machines vary almost that much. Saturn has eighty-three times more surface than the earth, and more than seven hundred and fifty times the earth's volume.

SURFACE ASPECTS AND CONSTITUTION

It is not at all certain that Saturn, more than Jupiter, has any solid surface. Indeed, it is almost certain that it has not. It is surrounded by an atmosphere of great density, and we do not at any time see the surface of the planet. It is believed probable that it is at least largely in a liquid state, if not to a great extent even gaseous.

The planet is certainly not in any way dependent on the sun for the extraordinary heat that everything indicates it to have, and its surface is brighter than it is believed it could be if shining only by the reflected light of the sun. This does not mean that Saturn is self-luminous; but it is nearly certain that it is extremely hot and glowing, and its brightness may be in part due to its own internal fires and the extremely luminous and dense atmosphere that surrounds it. It receives one hundred times less heat and light from the sun than we do. If it depended entirely upon the sun for its heat, the temperature would be nearly three hundred degrees below zero, Fahrenheit. It is probably not only very hot itself, but its heavy atmospheric envelope perhaps allows comparatively little heat to escape.

Its surface is belted and spotted somewhat after the manner of Jupiter's, but, being so much farther from us than Jupiter, it does not disclose its surface features with the same distinctness. Apparently it is much less turbulent than Jupiter; but even this we are not quite certain of, and it may seem more placid because we do not so well see its agitations.

Like all the outer planets, it differs in its constitution from the earth and the other inner planets. Its atmosphere contains compounds with which we are not familiar, and the body of the planet itself is rarer and lighter, and less condensed, and in a much earlier stage of evolution than the earth and the small planets so comparatively near us.

DAY AND NIGHT

The length of Saturn's day, or its period of rotation on its axis, is about ten hours and a quarter. Like Jupiter, it has slightly different rates of rotation in different latitudes, thus showing its lack of solidity. The rate of rotation has been determined, as in the case of Jupiter, by observation of the spots on its surface, which, while they are not exactly permanent, yet remain apparently in the same positions for months and even years at a time, and are thus sufficiently stable to measure a rotation of so short a time as ten hours.

Whirling over at this rate would cause the sun to appear to skim across the sky very swiftly as viewed from Saturn. In size, it would not seem more than three times as large as Venus at her brightest seems to us, and every minute it would cover a distance about equal to the diameter of the full moon as we see it. In an hour it would seem to move more than six times as far as the distance between the "pointers." At the time of Saturn's equinox the little five-hour day, followed by the equally short night, must present a lively aspect with the sun racing thus swiftly across the sky in daylight and the stars sweeping as swiftly over at night. If things remain as they now are, it will be a splendid panorama for the people there when, in the far-distant future, Saturn may have cooled and solidified sufficiently to maintain life somewhat as we know it. The earth, though, and Venus and Mars would be from Saturn only telescopic objects to eyes like ours, and Jupiter no brighter than he is to us. Thus does our brother Saturn pay the price of his remoteness from the rest of the solar family.

THE RINGS AND MOONS OF SATURN

But the circling stars and the swift-moving sun are the least part of the splendid spectacle that might be seen from Saturn. He is surrounded with no less than ten moons of more or less imposing size, and in addition has three rings circling around with him, composed of myriads of small satellites, together forming a band the outer diameter of which is something more than twenty-one times broader than the diameter of the earth. These are the famous rings of Saturn, the only objects of their kind in the solar system, intensely interesting to scientific observers, wonderful to the curious, and splendidly beautiful to everybody. It is this profusion of rings and moons that entitles

Saturn to be called, as he often has been, the most spectacular of all the planets.

The outer ring is nearly ten thousand miles broad, and is separated from the next one by a space of about seventeen hundred miles. The second ring is nearly eighteen thousand miles across. It is very bright on the outer edge, but gradually grows less so, until, with a not very perceptible division, it fades into the inner ring, which is but slightly luminous, and is called the crape ring. This is about nine thousand miles broad and nearly ten thousand miles from Saturn. This gradual fading of the rings to a dusky hue toward the center, and then the blackness of the space between them and the planet, gives them from certain points of view a nest-like appearance; and my first impression of Saturn, when I saw him through the telescope, was that he was nestling in a concave body of light—an appearance that is intensified by his extreme flatness at the poles.

Notwithstanding the imposing breadth of these rings, they are less than a hundred miles in thickness. They are, in fact, nothing more than an untold number of tiny satellites revolving about Saturn in the same plane and close enough together to appear, at the distance they are from us, as if they were one body. Just how close they are together, and how they appear when near by, we do not yet know. It was first shown by mechanical laws that they *must* be composed of separate bodies; the spectroscope shows that they *are*; and it has recently been thought that they have even been *seen* to be so through a telescope.

Being all in the same plane, they form a flat, broad, thin ring, so thin that when the edge of the ring is turned toward us we cannot see them at all. We never see them at their full breadth. If we did, Saturn would be much brighter at times than he ever is. The plane in which they revolve is the plane of Saturn's equator; and the axis of Saturn, with the rings, has a tilt of twenty-seven degrees in his orbit. The result of this is that at the time of Saturn's equinoxes the edge of the rings is turned toward us, and they practically disappear. Half-way between the equinoxes they are open again as far as they ever are to our view. This is why Saturn alternates in brightness. The times of his equinoxes occur every fourteen and eight-tenths years, and he is then alternately in Leo and Aquarius and is least bright. The times at which the rings are most open occur at intervals of the same length, and he is then alternately in Scorpio and Taurus and at his brightest.

SATURN AND ITS RINGS

Photographed at Mt. Wilson by E. E. Barnard, the six exposures being made on one plate.

It is believed that Saturn's rings were never a part of the planet, but are mere particles of cosmic materials which happened to be left over, and which he has gathered up by his force of gravity and compelled to revolve about him.

Saturn, more fortunate than Jupiter, has escaped the unimaginative naming of his moons by number, though one would think that, having such a numerous offspring, a shortage in names would be more likely to occur in his than in any other planet family. They all have names more or less connected with the great god whose name the planet bears, and are, in order of their distance from Saturn: Mimas, Enceladus, Tethys, Dione, Rhea, Titan, Hyperion, Japetus, Phœbe, and Themis. The largest and brightest of them all is Titan. It is larger than our moon, which is one of the large moons in the solar system, or than Mercury, and is not much smaller than Mars. It is more than three-quarters as large as all the other moons of Saturn put together. Naturally, it was the first to be discovered, and was under observation as long ago as 1655. Rhea and Japetus are next in size, and were discovered in 1671–72; Dione and Tethys were both discovered in 1684, and Enceladus and Mimas in 1789.

Until 1848 seven moons were all that were known to belong to Saturn. In that year little Hyperion, whose diameter, it is thought, can hardly exceed two hundred miles, came into our view. A little more than fifty years later (in 1898) Phœbe made her bright mark on a photographic plate at Harvard, and was caught. By tracing her from one plate to another her orbit was computed, her probable size determined, and practically all that is known about her was found out before she was seen, which was not until 1904. She is not much larger than a good-sized mountain, but is a unique and interesting little satellite that, far outside of the paths of any of the other moons, circles in an eccentric orbit around Saturn in an opposite direction from the rest of the satellites, and thus gives rise to many interesting astronomical speculations. Themis, also a tiny body, was discovered in the same way in 1906, and is thought to be the smallest body in the solar system. Titan is the only one of this group of satellites whose true disc we can see even with a telescope. Only one other (Rhea) can be seen in transit across the planet. The others are not much more than bright points of light, while Phœbe and Themis are almost at the limit of visibility.

On account of their great distance from the sun Saturn's moons are, of course, not very bright, and all of them put together do not give one-tenth as much light to Saturn as we receive from our moon. But, such as they are, they may some day be very useful to Saturn as a means of illumination. Receiving as he does a hundred times less light from the sun than we do, he may be some day much in need of the light reflected from all his rings and moons.

SEASONS

The seasons on Saturn are somewhat like ours in the succession of spring, summer, autumn, and winter; but the inclination of its axis to its orbit being twenty-seven degrees instead of twenty-three and a half, as ours is, each season is much more accentuated than ours. The sun climbs higher during the northern summer, and sinks correspondingly lower during the winter. But in length Saturn's seasons are very different from ours. Like his year, they are about twenty-nine and one-half times as long as ours. Each one is more than seven years long. Even the agreeable seasons might grow monotonous to one in that time; but to be spinning through the rapidly alternating days and nights of Saturn during seven long years of winter is a situation that one does not care to contemplate. It is with world personalities as with human personalities: however much we may admire their superior grandeur, when we consider details we would not change places with them.

The symbol of Saturn is an ancient scythe (♄), which gets its appropriateness from the fact that the deity of that name was the special protector of agriculture.

XV

URANUS

Venus, Mars, Jupiter, and Saturn, brilliant beauties that they are, have always been distinguished features of the heavenly view. The records of Mercury do not go back so far as those of these more easily seen planets, yet there is no reason to think that he has not been always known, though less widely, perhaps, than the four planets more frequently in view. To Uranus belongs the distinction of being the first planet that was *discovered*—a distinction that one cannot help but feel was too long delayed, for it did not come until 1781. For ages and ages his lovely pale beams had been shining down upon us from his little disc, no fainter in brilliancy than many a sixth-magnitude star (a degree of brightness which we think is within the limit of good vision, even in these days), and no human being had been conscious that this bright body was only another member of the solar family, circling with the rest of us around our parent, the sun, and having nothing in common with the far-off stars among which we had numbered him. Nineteen times he had been charted as a fixed star before his identity was suspected, and after he became known to us as a planet he was, by means of these charts, traced back for one hundred and thirty years, and much information was thus gained concerning his orbit and movements.

Uranus was not, however, discovered through observation of his movement among the stars. A view of his actual disc was caught by the musician and astronomer, Herschel, as he gleaned with his telescope in that part of the sky where the planet lay, one hundred and seventy-one years after the invention of that aid to vision. It was at first thought that a comet had been discovered, but later investigation showed a much more important member of the solar system, and the discovery of a new planet was announced.

George III. was then King of England, and the loyal Herschel called the planet *Georgium Sidus* in honor of that monarch. Fortunately, the world-wide interest in this newly discovered body saved it from so local an appellation, and it finally came to be called after Uranus, the father of Saturn, a name somewhat more in keeping with its place among the planets. In England, however, a very commendable loyalty to Herschel has resulted in the planet's sometimes being called Herschel, after its discoverer, and we see this name often in English books on astronomy, especially the older books; but Uranus is now the generally accepted name.

The symbol of the planet as it appears in all almanacs—at least in all English almanacs—is a capital H with a planet swinging from the cross-bar in the letter, thus ♅. And to this extent the discovery of the planet by Herschel is commemorated. In American almanacs the symbol is contracted into this figure ♅.

It is a matter for regret that Uranus does not come more easily within our view; for he is a very beautiful planet, pale green in color, and unlike any of the others in his aspect. There are, however, very few persons nowadays who can see him without the aid of at least a small glass, and to most of us he must ever remain a body with which we can have no personal acquaintance. None the less he must have an interest to us such as attaches always to anything so closely related to us, and sharing with us a common origin and a common destiny. To those who have unusually keen vision—or a small telescope—there will be much pleasure in viewing the planet. But even to those who have not these facilities for seeing, it ought to be interesting to know in what region of the skies this far-off member of our family dwells, what his wanderings are, and something of his personality and habits.

It requires a few days more than eighty-four years for Uranus to make one revolution around the sun, so that he moves even more slowly than Saturn from one constellation to another; and if we could only see him more easily, he would be scarcely more difficult to keep track of than a fixed star. He remains in each constellation somewhere near seven years and his change of place in the skies amounts in one year to but little more than four degrees, which is less than the distance between the pointers.

Since Uranus was discovered he has made one circuit of the skies, which he finished in 1865, and he is now (1912) more than half-way around on another. His position now is in Capricornus, nearly twenty degrees east of the "milk dipper" in Sagittarius, and for the next quarter of a century he can be seen by any who have eyes, or a glass, to accomplish this during the summer evenings. Each year he will be about seven degrees farther east. He is, however, still pretty far south of the equator, and not so easily seen as he will be when he reaches that part of the ecliptic which runs somewhat higher in the skies. Even an opera-glass will bring Uranus into the view of many persons. His path deviates very little from the line of the ecliptic—never quite so much as half a degree. The knowledge of this makes it less difficult to find him.

The synodic period of Uranus is about three hundred and sixty-nine days, so that an opposition occurs about four or five days later each year. He was in opposition this year (1912) on July 24th. In 1913 an opposition will take place on July 29th, and in 1914 on August 2d, and oppositions will occur about four days later each year thereafter.

Uranus is twice as far from the sun as Saturn is, and nineteen times as far as the earth. Its mean distance from the sun is 1,784,732,000 miles, and at this distance more than two hours and a half would be required for light to travel from the sun to the planet. Viewed from the planet, the sun would appear only about two and a half times larger than Jupiter appears to us, and the earth would be a very small telescopic body, if, indeed, it would be visible at all. Even at this great distance from the sun, and with the sun showing so small as it does, the planet would still have more than a thousand times as much light as we get from our moon, and so in this respect might be fairly comfortably provided for even for eyes constructed like those of human beings. The heat the sun's radiant energy furnishes to Uranus is, from our point of view, almost a negligible quantity. If there were no other source of supply, the normal temperature of the planet would be more than three hundred degrees below zero, Fahrenheit. There is no reason to think, however, that this is the temperature that prevails on Uranus. As far as we can tell, it has a dense and extensive atmosphere, and probably very considerable internal heat.

Uranus is smaller than either Jupiter or Saturn; but it is much larger than Mars, Venus, Mercury and the earth combined. Its diameter is nearly thirty-three thousand miles. Its volume is sixty-five times as great as that of the earth; but its mass is only about fourteen times the mass of the earth, which shows it to be a very much expanded body. It is slightly more dense than water, but only about two-tenths as dense as the earth. Its force of gravity is small for so large a body—only about nine-tenths that of the earth.

There is every indication that the planet is not a solid body at all, and that it is, perhaps, largely vapor. We undoubtedly cannot see the surface of it; but through the telescope it faintly shows the same belted appearance that we see on Jupiter and on Saturn, though it is difficult to see the belted region, which is near the equator, because the axis of the planet is so inclined to its orbit that much of the time the poles are pointed almost toward us. The spectroscope indicates something of the same materials in its atmosphere that the other large and faraway planets have, and there is no reason to doubt that the planet is in a much earlier stage of development than any of the terrestrial planets.

We really know nothing certainly about the rotation of Uranus; but there seems to be some indication that, like Jupiter and Saturn, it revolves swiftly—in perhaps ten or twelve hours, and hence has a very short day and night. The great inclination of its axis must make its seasons so abnormal, from our point of view, that it is difficult to understand what they are. Moreover, the planet is, at this stage of its development, so far from being a habitable body, for beings such as we know anything about, that the subject of its seasons seems not very important or interesting.

It seems but fitting that this vapory, pale green planet should have satellites with the fairy names of Ariel, Umbriel, Titania, and Oberon. One can forgive a good many utilitarian feats in nomenclature for the sake of these charmingly appropriate names for the satellites of Uranus. Titania and Oberon were discovered in 1787 by Herschel, the discoverer of the planet. They are not very much farther from Uranus than our moon is from us, and are easily seen with a telescope. Titania, the nearer to Uranus and the larger, is probably about one thousand miles in diameter; and Oberon is not very much smaller. In 1852 Umbriel and Ariel were discovered. They are both smaller and nearer to Uranus than either of the two first discovered, and are seen with considerable difficulty, because of their proximity to the larger and brighter body of the planet. There is not, however, very much difference between any of the four in real brightness.

XVI

NEPTUNE

It is rather curious to what extent we have a feeling of kinship with Neptune, notwithstanding he dwells forever in far-off space where we cannot expect even to have a glimpse of him without the aid of a telescope. Uranus, the other very distant planet, is so nearly within the limit of ordinary vision that we have always a hope that, by some lucky chance of situation or atmosphere, we may some day be able to see him face to face, and know for ourselves what manner of planet this is which, though a member of our own cosmic family, remains always just beyond easy exchange of glances with us; and so we in a measure keep a lookout for him that gives us a sense of his reality.

With Neptune there can be no feeling of this sort to keep us with a lively interest in him, and yet he is hardly less real to us than Uranus, and we have a more intimate sense of nearness to him than we have for any fixed star. Far away as he is, the distance between us is short compared with the many trillions of miles farther that we must go to reach the nearest star, and in thinking of him we always have a sense of this. Then, however aloof he may keep himself from this cozy little bunch of planets near the sun, of which the earth is one, he is still of the same parentage with us, and his life history is part of our family history, so that we can never feel indifferent to what concerns him.

Close as Neptune is to us in kinship and distance, as astronomical distances go, we never knew of his existence until sixty-six years ago. He is to us almost a recent arrival in the solar domain, but we know that he has been here as long as we have; and whether he was detached before we were from the great nebula which gave birth to us all, or at about the same time, we know that for long ages before there were eyes on the earth to see him he was, as he still is, circling slowly and majestically around our common center of control.

The discovery of Neptune in 1846 created truly a sensation in astronomical circles. And, unlike most sensational happenings, it fully justified the extreme interest it aroused. The computation that led to it was a mathematical triumph, and the final result was a most splendidly convincing proof of the theory of gravitation. For the place of this hitherto unknown planet was found by means of computations based on the fact that at certain times Uranus went a little out of his way, thus showing some disturbing body outside of his orbit pulling him slightly from the course he would otherwise take. The deviation was not much—only about one and three-fourths of a minute, which is equal to about one-seventeenth of the apparent diameter of the moon, or one-sixth of the distance between Mizar and Alcor, situated at the bend of the handle of the Big Dipper, two stars that it is difficult for some eyes to separate.[7] But this slight irregularity of Uranus was enough to set at least two able men at work in an effort to locate the disturbing cause. These two men were Adams, of England, and Leverrier, of France.

The result of Adams's work was announced to the Astronomer Royal in England in the autumn of 1845; but the actual search for the planet in the place predicted was delayed until the following summer. In the mean time Leverrier had completed his work and had communicated with astronomers in Berlin, directing them where to look for the planet. The facilities for that sort of work were then better in Berlin than in England; and within half an hour after the search was begun, on the night of September 23, 1846, the new planet was discovered a little more than half a degree from the exact position Leverrier had found for it. It was first recognized as having a sensible disc, and within a day its motion was apparent. No wonder the astronomical world was thrilled by this achievement!

Although the planet was actually discovered by following the directions of Leverrier, it was found that it might have been seen months before if the English astronomers had shown more promptness in using the computations of Adams; and there has always been a disposition among astronomers, both in France and in England, to give both men credit for their extraordinary achievement, though, naturally, there is somewhat more stress laid upon the work of each in his own country. The newly discovered body was at first named for its discoverer, Leverrier, but a sense of justice to Adams prevailed to such an extent that in the end a less commemorative name was chosen, and the planet was called after Neptune, the son of Saturn and the brother of Jupiter—a name more fitting, on the whole, for a member of this planet family, whose other members all bear the names of some of the ancient deities. The trident (♆), Neptune's three-pronged spear, is the symbol of the planet.

The mean distance of Neptune from the sun is more than two and a half billion miles (2,790,000,000), and his orbit is so nearly circular that the variation between his perihelion and aphelion distance is only about fifty million miles. His orbit is, in fact, less eccentric than that of any other planet except Venus. His immense distance from the sun, of course, deprives him of any great amount of heat or light from that source as compared with the other planets. The sun would appear to an observer on Neptune a little smaller than Venus appears to us. But so great is the intensity of its radiance that even as so diminutive a sun as that it would give to Neptune more than six hundred times as much light as our full moon gives to us. This, however, would be as much as nine hundred times less light than we get from the sun. Such light as the planet receives from the sun reaches it after a journey of a little more than four hours.

Of the heat the planet has, either inherent or acquired from the sun, we do not know much. The normal temperature at that distance from the sun would be more than three hundred and sixty degrees below zero, Fahrenheit, and there is not much to indicate in what state the planet is with reference to its own heat. Investigations thus far made do not show it to be so intensely hot as Jupiter and Saturn undoubtedly are; but with its heavily vapor-laden atmosphere it could not have the frigidity normal to a black, unprotected body at its distance from the sun.

Neptune is thought to have an immense atmosphere, and, like the other outer planets, one of a composition not wholly familiar to us. Consequently we do not know as yet just what this atmosphere does for the planet. It has a fairly good reflecting power, though the planet, on the whole, is darker in color than Jupiter or Saturn. Its color is of that bluish cast which sometimes suggests a leaden appearance. The color, as well as the fact that Neptune is denser than any of the other outer planets, indicates that it may be in a more advanced stage of development than at least Jupiter and Saturn are, and perhaps than Uranus is.

That Neptune has made greater progress toward solidity (though it is still very far from that state) than the other outer planets is suggested also by its size; for, as we have seen, the smaller planets develop more rapidly than the larger ones. The diameter of Neptune is a little less than thirty thousand (29,827) miles. The planet is somewhat smaller, therefore, than Uranus, and much smaller than Jupiter or Saturn. But as compared with the earth, the largest of the inner planets, it is a vastly greater body. Its mass is seventeen times more than that of the earth; its surface is as much as sixteen times more extensive than the earth's; and its volume is more than eighty times greater than the volume of the earth.

Of the time of Neptune's rotation on its axis very little is known. That little, however, indicates a slower rotation than the other planets seem to have, and the alternations of day and night on Neptune are, therefore, probably less swift than on Jupiter and on Saturn. The planet is too far away for us to see its surface markings with any distinctness, but there are indirect processes by which we can get approximate information concerning the facts about rotation. One of these processes is by observation of the motions of the satellites. Of these useful bodies Neptune, fortunately, has one—a very excellent moon about the size of our own. It has some eccentricities, such as revolving about the planet in the opposite direction from that which the more conventional satellites follow, and having an orbit a good deal inclined to the plane of the equator of the parent body. But it is a very interesting moon to astronomers, and will no doubt in time help to make clear some things in the history of Neptune which are now not quite understood.

Being so far from the sun, Neptune moves, of course, very slowly in comparison with the nearer planets, though his speed is at the rate of three and a half miles a second, which, after all, does not denote any high degree of sluggishness. His change of position in the sky amounts to a little more than two degrees a year; so that in an ordinary lifetime he does not make any very great progress along the zodiac.

When Neptune was discovered he had just left the constellation Capricornus, and in the sixty-six years that his movements have been followed he has passed through Aquarius, Pisces, Aries, Taurus, and is now (1912) in Gemini, very near Castor and Pollux. The time required for his circuit around the sun is nearly one hundred and sixty-five (164.6) years, so that he remains for about thirteen years in each constellation. He will complete one sidereal period, dating from the time of his discovery, in the year 2011.

The apparent motion of Neptune is direct a little more than six months in the year, and retrograde a little more than five months, so that it seems to present the old mental arithmetic problem of the climber that fell back so much every time after he had climbed a certain number of feet. But the falling back in the case of Neptune is an illusion, as we know. He keeps straight on in his journey, as we may see if we watch him from year to year, and his change of position is so slight during any year that the change of direction is hardly noticeable.

Neptune is as bright as an eighth-magnitude star, and it is possible to see him with a good field-glass. The difficulty is in distinguishing him from a star, for his disc does not show except through a telescope. If one has such a glass, however, it will be worth while to direct it toward that part of the ecliptic just under Castor and Pollux any time within the next two or three years, and a sight of this yet strange brother planet may be the reward. He will be in opposition on January 14, 1913, and thereafter about two days later each year.

XVII

THE LITTLE PLANETS, OR THE ASTEROIDS

The asteroids, or minor planets, are situated almost wholly in the vast space between Mars and Jupiter. Their orbits are very irregular, both as to shape and situation; but, so far as is known, only two of them pass beyond the orbit of Jupiter, and only one has been discovered which at any point in its journey around the sun comes nearer than the orbit of Mars.

The minor planets are called by astronomers almost indifferently asteroids or planetoids. "Asteroids" is probably the name by which they are most popularly known. But because they are in fact simply little bodies that revolve about the sun as the planets do, "planetoids" seems to be more truly descriptive of them, and it is the word I have chosen to use here.

It was early noted that, except in one instance, the planets seemed to show in their distance from the sun something like a mathematical progression. Struck by this appearance, an astronomer named Bode worked it out into a formula, known ever since as Bode's law, though the idea seems to have originated with another astronomer. One almost always sees it mentioned in any work dealing with this phase of planetary history, and it is especially interesting because of the part it played in the discovery of the planetoids. It was as follows: Beginning with nothing for Mercury, add three for Venus, twice three, or six, for the earth, twelve for Mars, and continue thus to double the number for each planet out to and including Saturn. Then to each one of the numbers so obtained add four, and the numbers resulting will very nearly represent the relative distances of the planets from the sun. Thus:

0	3	6	12	24	48	96	192	384
4	4	4	4	4	4	4	4	4
4	7	10	16	28	52	100	196	388

The exception was that at the fifth number, 28, there was no planet to correspond, and Jupiter was nearly twice as far away from Mars as it should have been to conform to the law, thus leaving room for another planet to occupy the allotted position and fill out this very beautiful progression.

About nine years after this law was set forth Uranus was discovered circling out in space far beyond Saturn, and was found to conform to the law in a most satisfactory manner, its distance being approximately twice that of Saturn. With such close accord between the actual distances and the prescribed distances of the planets from the sun, and with the one exception leaving almost exactly the space allotted by Bode's law for another planet, astronomers naturally had a very strong feeling that there must be another planet between Mars and Jupiter. They accordingly set to work to prove this, if possible, and to find what had become of this lost member of the planet family, if it ever existed.

As a result of this work, on January 1, 1801, the first planetoid was discovered, and in rapid succession many like it were found, until now many hundreds are known to astronomers. Their discovery seemed at first almost a certain confirmation of Bode's law, and the fact that where one large planet should have been found there proved to be such a swarm of small ones could be accounted for in no other way than to suppose that something had happened in the making of the planet. At any rate, the promulgation of Bode's law was the direct cause of the search for the missing planet which led to the discovery of the planetoids. And this is the only reason why Bode's law has continued to be mentioned in the history of the planets. For it was no real law, it had no scientific foundation, and its conformity to the facts of the relative distances of the planets was only one of those very interesting and singular coincidences that startle one for the moment into thinking that there is some scientific significance in them. Another example of such a coincidence is in the fact that the mass of any given planet exceeds the total mass of all the planets of any less mass than itself.

In less than half a century after the discovery of the first planetoid, Neptune was discovered at a distance not at all corresponding to that indicated by Bode's law. It was not nearly far enough away, and yet, strangely enough, it was by taking Bode's law into consideration that the position was indicated which finally led to the discovery of the planet. So while Bode's law has been found to be no law at all, it is, nevertheless, entitled to some mention because of its having thus stimulated research that has had such important results.

No really satisfactory and final explanation of the present state of the planetoids has ever been given. At one time it was suggested that another planet had originally existed in the space between Mars and Jupiter, and through some catastrophe had been shattered into the small bodies that now occupy that space. But this has been shown to be impossible.

It is now thought probable that in the original nebula the matter forming the planetoids might have been prevented from condensing into a planet by the powerful gravitative influence of Jupiter. This influence, however, was not sufficiently strong to bring them entirely under his control. Even yet he pulls some of them five or six degrees out of the path they otherwise would take when they venture within the limits of his domain; but he does not capture them, so they have been left to circle around the sun as mere fragments of bodies, with no force to combine and make a world, no mass to hold an atmosphere, and with nothing to prevent them from quickly condensing and from radiating all their heat into space. They are, in the main, just cold, dark, lifeless rocks and lumps of matter whirling through space in a maze of interlacing orbits, some of them almost as far from the sun as Jupiter and some almost as near as Mars—one, indeed, a little nearer than Mars at certain times—but most of them swarming more thickly about half-way between Mars and Jupiter, not far from the place that Bode's law assigned to a planet.

After the first planetoid was discovered and had been observed for a few weeks, it was lost and had to be rediscovered by means of mathematical computation of its orbit. Where this computation showed that it ought to be, there it was found, on the very last day of the same year, 1801. Early the next year another body of the same sort was discovered, two years later another was found, and still three years later a fourth came into view. These four were the only ones known in this branch of the solar family for nearly forty years thereafter.

In 1845 another period of discovery commenced, and has ever since continued, until there are now between six and seven hundred of these little bodies that have disclosed their right to be known as members of the sun's family. It is probable that there may be still many more of them, since a new one comes to light every now and then on a photographic plate, and there is no indication of any limit to the number that may thus appear.

It is likely that about all have been discovered that can be seen even with a telescope, for a fairly systematic and thorough search has been made of the heavens for this purpose during the last half-century. This work has resulted in a continually decreasing number of discoveries, until this method of search has finally been practically abandoned. But it not infrequently happens that in photographing the stars a little trail of light is discovered on the plate, showing that some heavenly body with sensible motion has been caught on it. And this usually proves to be a new planetoid. No matter how long a photographic plate is exposed, the fixed stars imprint themselves on it only as

119

points of light. When the impression is a little streak of light instead of a dot, the object is shown to be in motion, and is either a planetoid, a satellite, or a comet. The fixed stars would make a trail also if the photographic apparatus were not regulated by clockwork, so as to follow the star in its apparent daily motion across the skies. The planets and other bodies in the solar system are sufficiently near to have a sensible motion in addition to the motion caused by the rotation of the earth, which is the only motion we have to take into account in dealing with the aspects of the stars.

The first planetoid discovered was called Ceres, the next one Pallas, the third Juno, and the fourth Vesta. This pretty custom of naming them after the gods and goddesses of mythology was continued, with some variations, until perhaps three hundred had been so christened. But the number of them became too prodigious; and when so many began to swarm into view, waiting to be named, the utilitarian method of designating them simply by numbers in the order of their discovery was adopted. The only distinguishing feature of so numbering them is that each number is placed in a little circle. Thus Ceres is ①, Pallas ②, and so on. Those of them that have any special claim to distinction, however, are still referred to by their own names, if they have any, in spite of this most orderly attempt to make them fit for easy reference in a list.

There are so many of the planetoids, and they are so minute, that even after they have been discovered they are frequently lost again. Hence it is sometimes uncertain when they register themselves on the photographic plates whether they are really new to us or have been known before. In such cases they are named temporarily after the letters of the alphabet, and, when the alphabet is exhausted, a second letter is added. Thus A to Z, then AB to AZ, BC to BZ, and so on in a sort of "round." Sometimes these combinations of letters become the fixed designation of a planetoid, as a nickname sometimes clings to a person. And thus it happens that we sometimes read of one in particular of these little bodies that is conspicuous for the great eccentricity of its orbit, called "WD." The letters are not its initials, but its nickname. It really has no name other than its number in the list; but it became famous while it was temporarily designated as "WD," and thus it continues to be called.

The aid of a telescope is necessary in order to see the planetoids, though it is said that Vesta, under very favorable conditions, sometimes comes within the limit of visibility. She is the brightest of them all, though not the largest, and her brilliancy is the subject of much interesting speculation among astronomers, who have not yet been able to account for it. She seems from her excessive brightness to be covered with clouds; and yet it is manifestly impossible that so small a body could have held an atmosphere throughout these long ages, though clouds presuppose an atmosphere. No doubt, in time this mystery of Vesta's brilliancy will be made plain. Bright as she is in proportion to her size, and even if she sometimes can be seen, one cannot reasonably expect anything very brilliant to our view from a body not much more than a hundred miles in diameter, shining by reflected light, nearly two hundred million miles away.

Ceres, as far as we yet know, is the largest of the planetoids, and may be something more than four hundred miles in diameter. Juno is somewhere near the same size. Pallas is about two hundred miles in diameter, and Vesta about one hundred and eighteen. No doubt, these four were the first to be discovered, because they are the largest and so the easiest to be seen. At any rate, no others yet seen exceed them in size, and some of the more lately discovered are not more than fifteen or twenty miles in diameter. Many of those discovered by photography are doubtless even smaller than these, and are, perhaps, mere meteors in size. The combined mass of all those discovered up to this time is far smaller than that of any of the large planets, or even than that of our moon. Their mass cannot, of course, really be measured, because they are too small to have any perceptible gravitative effect on other bodies, and mass can only be determined by the influence of one body on another. But we do know that their aggregate mass, if it exceeded a certain limit, would show some disturbing effect on Mars; and, since it does not do this, we know that all of them taken together would make an extremely insignificant body.

While the planetoids all revolve around the sun in the same manner and in the same direction as the planets do, yet they are very erratic in their courses, and do not all keep within the narrow limits of the zodiac through which—happily for our convenient observation—the larger bodies travel. The orbits of many of them are extremely elliptical, while some are almost circles; and their inclination to the ecliptic varies from almost nothing to nearly fifty degrees. If one could catch from one side a view of them all together, they would have much the appearance in space of a flock of swallows, the individuals darting this way and that, passing above and below one another in such intricate sweeps and sinuosities that it would be impossible to keep track of them separately. And yet time has brought these apparently tangled orbits into such nice adjustment that the little bodies can continue to cross and recross each other's paths with no danger of interference from each other. Such collisions as there may have been occurred in the very beginning of their careers. Such of them as came into collision then traveled on together as one body until accommodation was made for all.

One of the most wide-wandering of these tiny bodies has been named Eros, after the little god of love, more commonly known as Cupid. It has a particular interest for us, because of all the heavenly bodies it at times comes nearer to us than any except the moon and an occasional comet. At its nearest it is within fourteen million miles of the earth, which is more than ten million miles nearer than the closest approach of Venus, the nearest of the large planets.

This little body was thus near us in 1894; but we did not then know this, for Eros was not discovered until 1898. After its discovery, however, it was traced back on many photographic plates, and the fact that it had been in our neighborhood was learned. For untold ages it has been making these visits to us every thirty-seven years, and we have known nothing of them. Its next near approach will be in 1931, and it will continue to come thereafter every thirty-seven years. Now that we know about them, these visits are not only pleasant to contemplate, but it is expected that when they occur the planetoid will be of great scientific value to us in helping to determine more surely and accurately the exact distance of the sun.

The planetoids, though so minute and of no value as a spectacle, have been, and still are, very useful little bodies to us in a scientific way. In addition to furnishing an easy means of measuring the distance of the sun, they promise to throw some light on various questions of physics in which the planets, too, are involved. The brilliancy of Vesta, for instance, which has been mentioned, and the unaccountable variability in the brightness of some others of them have yet to be adjusted to known physical laws. Even the extreme eccentricity of some of their orbits, and the large tilt of some of them to the ecliptic, may be suggestive in finally solving certain planetary problems, for these impish little bodies are far from conforming to the regular ways of the planets, and there is, of course, some mechanical reason for their apparent waywardness.

XVIII

CONCLUSION

The great variety of beauty that the planets present to us is sufficient to keep us always interested in them, when once we have acquired an acquaintance with them. Rarely is there an evening when some one of them does not enhance the charm of the splendid spectacle of the sky in which all the heavenly bodies save the sun have a part. Their greater brilliancy often brings them into view before the stars have begun to glow in the evening, and prolongs our sight of them after the rays of the sun have blotted out the light of the stars in the morning. Thus they are always single in their loveliness, and always hold a distinguished place in the midst of the brilliant company of the stars.

Having considered these brilliant bodies individually and in detail, as we have, we ought by this time to be able to identify any one of them that shows itself in the evening sky, and to have a pretty fair notion of the general character and peculiarities of each. But even if one does not much care for detailed information concerning them, or, before seeking that, prefers first to become familiar with their appearance, a quick and sure recognition of them may be had by noting their positions and their very striking individual aspects as set forth in the preceding chapters.

On seeing a bright object in the sky that does not seem to be a familiar star, simply stop and look at it. Does it twinkle? If it does not, it is a planet. If it is more than forty-five degrees from the sun, or if it is seen at a time when the sun has been down more than three hours, then it is neither Mercury nor Venus, and must be either Mars, Jupiter, or Saturn. Is it very bright and pinkish in tone? Then it is Jupiter. Is it very bright and quite red? It is Mars, not far from opposition. Is it not very bright, but small and rosy? Then it is Mars going toward conjunction. Is it yellow in tone and, while large and conspicuous, still not so very brilliant? It is Saturn.

If the planet we seek to name is nearer to the sun than forty-five degrees, but is still well above the horizon, it may be either of these three—Mars, Jupiter, Saturn—or it is Venus. If it is very bright and silvery, it is certainly Venus. If it is very low in the sky and very near the sun, it may be any one of the five visible planets. In such a position Mars will always be very small, and the others always larger than a first-magnitude star; and they may all twinkle a little—Mercury almost as much as a star. Their size will show them all (except Mars) as planets, but it will be somewhat more difficult to tell which is which than it is when they are higher up in the sky. The best thing to do in such circumstances is to look up their positions either in this book or in an almanac. The almanac will serve as a footman to announce them. The book, it is hoped, has so recorded their peculiarities and habits that either their appearance or their place will be sufficient to make them known.

In any event, the problem of identification in this position will not keep one long, for in a situation presenting these greater difficulties the planet will be visible for less than an hour after sundown. Besides, it is not likely at such times to attract one's involuntary attention, but when under observation in such a situation is usually sought out by those already somewhat informed as to the planet's habits and appearance, which will betray its identity. It is information of this sort that I have endeavored to give in these pages, and it is hoped that the reading of them will be the beginning of a long and intimate acquaintance with these charming and always interesting individuals.

Individuals the planets inevitably become to any one who learns to know them during the long, quiet nights in the country, or wherever an opportunity is afforded really to contemplate their peculiar traits and features. Like individuals of whatever kind, they impress different persons in different ways. As I have watched them from year to year I have come to have a very distinct impression of Jupiter as slow and majestic, and yet not lacking in joviality; Saturn as friendly, but reserved; Mars as sturdily brisk and busy; Venus as always gracious and smiling; and Mercury as irresponsible and roguish. Others might have an entirely different feeling in regard to them; but an intimate acquaintance with them, which is not wholly scientific, cannot fail to stamp them as in some sort individuals.

And when we consider that these interesting individuals are closely related members of our cosmic family, their ever-changing beauty of aspect, the history of their development and their affairs generally, gain a significance to us that no other heavenly bodies can have. The two groups of planets—the inner and the outer—are like two sets of children in a family: born of the same parent, but under very different circumstances, and in very different surroundings. Mars, the earth, Venus, and Mercury are all, as compared with the outer planets, small and dense, with more or less thin atmospheres and an abundance of heat and light. They all lie comparatively near to the sun, and are composed of the denser material lying near the center of the great nebula, which was the original form of the entire solar system. Probably denser to begin with than the others, they have, on account of their diminutive size, developed more rapidly and are further advanced toward the final state of solidity which we shall all attain in the end. Mercury, the smallest, is already old and seamed and hardened. Mars, the next in size, is well advanced, but still has an atmosphere and some other signs of vitality. Venus, though we know so little about her, has probably a long period of development yet before her; while this warm, nourishing earth, which seems to us the best one of them all, will probably for a still longer time than Venus hold its atmosphere and remain green and flourishing.

On the other side of the vast space which divides the two groups of the sun's family dwell Jupiter, Saturn, Uranus, and Neptune. They are all tremendous in volume, enveloped in immense atmospheres, far, far from our common source of heat and light, of comparatively slight density, and probably formed from the lighter material composing the outer edges of the parent nebula, and, because of their immense size, still in a very early stage of development. The two groups could scarcely seem more widely different if they belonged to different systems; but the members of each are all closely akin, and each one in its own way, determined by its size and environment, is developing toward the same end.

If there is life on any of these outer planets, it must be of a sort of which we have no conception. Jupiter and Saturn are probably red-hot, and could sustain nothing more cold-blooded than a race of salamanders, though why a race of intelligent salamanders should or should not exist there, is a question that one might make bold to answer according to one's fancy. Uranus and Neptune are smaller, and perhaps less hot than Jupiter and Saturn; but we really know very little about the state of their domestic affairs, and the little we do know in no way indicates a place of abode for any sort of intelligence conceivable to us. We can, however, conceive of a time in the far-distant ages when these four hot and vaporous planets may have become sufficiently condensed to have a solid crust, and yet have sufficient internal heat to moderate the frigid temperature that would be normal at their distance from the sun, and they might then support life even somewhat resembling and perhaps even more gloriously beautiful than that with which we are familiar.

Of the existence of life somewhat similar to ours on the smaller, near-by planets we may have something nearer a reasonable conception, though we are nowhere near the possession of any real knowledge concerning it. Mercury, we have every reason to think, cannot support life, mainly because of his lack of atmosphere; but also because of his long rotation, which affords no alternations of day and night, but leaves him with one side always burning-hot and the other inconceivably cold. Venus might very well have a climate not utterly unlike ours, and hence be habitable for beings somewhat resembling us, if she has, as she has long been thought to have, a heavier atmosphere than the earth has, and if she has alternations of day and night. But we have seen that, owing to the obscurity of the surface of Venus, our knowledge in regard to these conditions is far from certain, and we have little reason to have even speculative ideas concerning life there. With Mars it is a more open question. We can see that planet, and see it fairly well. It has an atmosphere and changes of seasons, and while it may not afford a climate that would be exactly attractive to us as a place of transmigration, it is not particularly unreasonable to let our fancy play over the rather pleasant speculation concerning the presence there of beings at least understandable by us, even if not wholly congenial.

Whatever each planet affords in the way of life and human interests, all of them must ever be to us the most interesting things in all nature, outside of our own earth, in the two regards already pointed out: first, as the most beautiful objects of vision among all the starry hosts, and, second, as our nearest kindred in this universe of suns and systems of worlds. Together the earth and they circle ceaselessly around and around the sun, following in nicely adjusted orbits that great luminary as it sweeps majestically on through space toward the beautiful Vega, itself a sun, and, so far as we now know, in this close companionship we shall continue until every planet and the sun itself has become cold and dark and lifeless. And then, perhaps, or even before the light of our system is finally extinguished, we may meet another wandering sun, and in the marriage of the two great bodies another system of worlds may be evolved of which we and the planets shall form a part.

SYMBOLS USED IN ALMANACS

☿ = Mercury.

♀ = Venus.

⊕ = Earth.

♂ = Mars.

♃ = Jupiter.

♄ = Saturn.

♅ or ♅ = Uranus.

♆ = Neptune.

● = New Moon.

☽ = First Quarter.

○ = Full Moon.

☾ = Last Quarter.

☉ = Sun.

♂ = Conjunction with the sun; or, in the case of two planets or a planet and the moon, near together.

☍ = Opposition.

□ = Quadrature.

Examples:

♂ ♂ ♀ = Mars and Venus near together.
♂° ♃ ☉ = Jupiter in opposition.
♂ ♃ ☉ = Jupiter in conjunction.
♂ ☿ ☉ Inf. = Mercury in inferior conjunction.
♂ ☿ ☉ Sup. = Mercury in superior conjunction.
♂ ♀ ☽ = Venus and Moon near together.